DOSAGE
and
SOLUTIONS

DOSAGE
and
SOLUTIONS

DOROTHY M. BLUME, R.N., B.S.N., M.S.N.

Assistant Professor of Nursing
The University of Texas Nursing School (System-wide)
Austin, Texas

F. A. DAVIS COMPANY
PHILADELPHIA

Manufactured in the United States of America.

Second Printing October 1970

Third Printing, March 1972

Library of Congress Catalog Card Number 70-94416

ISBN 0-8036-0950-7

PREFACE

This workbook is written primarily for students in professional nursing programs. The reader will also find it of value for in-service education programs, in refresher courses for inactive nurses, and as a desk reference for nurses administering medications wherever they are employed. When students are using this book, an early introduction to classroom laboratory problems with actual drugs and equipment is suggested.

This workbook offers a practical approach to learning to prepare drug dosages and solutions. The suggested methods of doing the calculations have been simplified to the use of three variations of ratio and proportion. However, the examples were selected to present the realistic and often difficult problems which may be encountered in preparing drugs and solutions for administration. Practices or problems no longer encountered were not included.

I wish to express sincere appreciation to the faculty members and many students of The University of Texas Nursing School (System-wide) for their encouragement and for their helpful suggestions, many of which were used in this workbook.

Dorothy M. Blume

CONTENTS

CHAPTER I

INTRODUCTION

Working dosage problems involves the calculation of the correct dosage to be administered to the patient, usually either orally or parenterally, in order to give the prescribed amount of a drug. Usually the physician will order the drug in numbers of grains, grams, or other units of *weight* measure. To administer the correct dosage, nurses often will need to convert this order to a number of tablets, capsules, minims, drams, ounces, milliliters, or other units of *volume or capacity* measure. A single ratio and proportion formula (hereafter referred to as Formula B) can be used to work all dosage problems.

Doing solutions problems involves determining how to prepare solutions, usually for topical use. There are two variations of solutions problems, but both can be solved by using a second ratio and proportion formula (hereafter referred to as Formula C).

In solving either dosage or solutions problems a third ratio and proportion formula (hereafter referred to as Formula A) may be used to determine equivalent values whenever necessary. This additional initial step may be necessary in order to limit the different units of measure in any proportion to two units of measure. One can say, for example, that 4 wheels : 1 car = 8 wheels : 2 cars. One cannot say, however, that 4 wheels : 1 car = 8 wheels : 2 bicycles. Therefore, if the physician orders aspirin grains 10 and the available tablets are labelled "0.3 gram," Formula A would be used first to convert either grains 10 to its gram equivalent or to convert 0.3 gram to its grains equivalent. Then, when using Formula B to determine how many tablets to give, tablets would be one unit of measure and either grains or grams the other unit of measure. A grain is an apothecaries' system unit of measure; a gram is a metric system unit of measure.

SYSTEMS OF MEASUREMENT

The American colonists brought to this country the use of the apothecaries' system of weights and measures which was then being used in England. England is now adopting use of the metric system which has long been the single lawful system in most European countries. Since World War II there has been a growing

1

tendency in the United States for doctors to order and for pharmaceutical companies to label drugs with the metric system units of measure. Learning to administer drugs would be greatly simplified if only the metric system were used. Until that time, however, nurses will need to know about three systems of measurement, the apothecaries', the metric, and the household systems. More complete tables and explanations of these three systems and approximate equivalents among the systems may be found in Appendix A. Further explanations are included throughout the workbook.

One thing should be emphasized before anyone becomes discouraged from consulting these lengthy tables. Almost all equivalents nurses will ever need to know can be determined by using ratio and proportion with the few equivalents listed in Table 1. Learn ratio and proportion and these equivalents backwards, forwards, and crosswise; then mastering dosage and solutions will be simple.

It is customary to use regular fractions for the apothecaries' system and decimal fractions for the metric system. To minimize the danger of error a zero is placed before the decimal point when writing a fraction of a metric unit.

Sometimes symbols are used to express apothecaries' units of measure. The most commonly used apothecaries' symbols are ʒ for dram and ℥ for ounce. Also, when using the apothecaries' units the numerical value or the quantity of a unit is often expressed in Roman numerals, usually in lower case letters. For example, five grains may be written as grains v; four drams as ʒiv or ʒīv; and six ounces as ℥vi or ℥vī.

Occasionally household measures are used for ordering dosages of medications. The quantity may be written in either Arabic or Roman numerals. For example, 15 drops may be written as 15 gtts. or as gtts. xv. Gtts. is an acceptable abbreviation for drops. See Appendix B for a list of abbreviations commonly used in the administration of medications.

RATIO AND PROPORTION

A proportion is an equation of equal fractions or ratios. For example, the ratios 1/2 and 4/8 are equal or 1 : 2 = 4 : 8. The first and fourth terms of a proportion are called the extremes and the second and third terms the means. The product of the means equals the product of the extremes.

```
            means
          ┌──────┐
          1 : 2 = 4 : 8                    1 x 8 = 8
          └──────────┘                     2 x 4 = 8
            extremes
```

Table 1. Most Frequently Used Approximate Equivalents

WEIGHT UNITS			FLUID UNITS		
Household	Metric	Apothecaries'	Apothecaries'	Metric	Household
	1 gram or 1000 milligrams or 1,000,000 micrograms	15 or 16 grains	15 or 16 minims	1 milliliter	15 or 16 drops
2 tablespoonfuls or 8 teaspoonfuls	30 or 32 grams	1 ounce or 8 drams	1 fluid ounce or 8 fluid drams	30 or 32 milliliters	2 tablespoonfuls or 8 teaspoonfuls
			1 pint or 16 fluid ounces	500 milliliters	2 glassfuls
	1 kilogram or 1000 grams	2.2 or 2.3 pounds (imperial or avoirdupois—not apothecaries')	1 quart	1000 milliliters or 1 liter	4 glassfuls
			1 gallon	4000 milliliters	

The terms of the two ratios of a proportion must correspond in relative value; for example, small is to small as large is to large, or small is to large as small is to large.

$$1 : 2 = 4 : 8$$

small : small = large : large ?

or

small : large = small : large ?

This correspondence, which is confusing enough when only numerical values are used, is more confusing when numerical values plus two units of measure are involved, as in dosage and solutions problems. For example, if 15 grains equals 1 gram, 30 grains equals how many grams?

$$
\begin{aligned}
15 \text{ gr.} : 1 \text{ Gm.} \quad &= \quad 30 \text{ gr.} : x \text{ Gm.} \\
15x \quad &= \quad 30 \\
x \quad &= \quad 2 \text{ Gm.; therefore, 30 gr. equals 2 Gm.}
\end{aligned}
$$

or

$$15 \text{ gr.} : 1 \text{ Gm.} \quad = \quad 30 \text{ gr.} : 2 \text{ Gm.}$$

Disregarding numerical values, the ratios in the above proportion correspond small : large = small : large, because grains are smaller units of measure than grams. Numerical values cannot be disregarded, however. Both the relative value of the units of measure and the relative value of the quantities of these units of measure must be considered. Otherwise, even when using the correct numerical values, the product of the means *may not equal* the product of the extremes, as shown below.

$$2 \times 30 = 60$$

$$15 \text{ gr.} : 2 \text{ Gm.} = 30 \text{ gr.} : 1 \text{ Gm.}$$

$$15 \times 1 = 15$$

Unless the proportion is stated properly the solutions to the problem will be *incorrect*, as shown below.

$$
\begin{aligned}
15 \text{ gr.} : x \text{ Gm.} &= 30 \text{ gr.} : 1 \text{ Gm.} \\
30x &= 15 \\
x &= 0.5 \text{ Gm.; therefore, 30 gr. equals 0.5 Gm.}
\end{aligned}
$$

There are several possible ways, as shown below, to state *correctly* any one proportion.

$$15 \text{ gr.} : 1 \text{ Gm.} = 30 \text{ gr.} : 2 \text{ Gm.}$$

or

$$15 \text{ gr.} : 30 \text{ gr.} = 1 \text{ gm.} : 2 \text{ Gm.}$$

or

$$30 \text{ gr.} : 2 \text{ Gm.} = 15 \text{ gr.} : 1 \text{ Gm.}$$

or

$$30 \text{ gr.} : 15 \text{ gr.} = 2 \text{ Gm.} : 1 \text{ Gm.}$$

or

$$1 \text{ Gm.} : 2 \text{ Gm.} = 15 \text{ gr.} : 30 \text{ gr.}$$

or

$$1 \text{ Gm.} : 15 \text{ gr.} = 2 \text{ Gm.} : 30 \text{ gr.}$$

or

$$2 \text{ Gm.} : 1 \text{ Gm.} = 30 \text{ gr.} : 15 \text{ gr.}$$

or

$$2 \text{ Gm.} : 30 \text{ gr.} = 1 \text{ Gm.} : 15 \text{ gr.}$$

There are just as many possible ways to state *incorrectly* any one proportion.

KNOWN VALUES FORMULAS

Avoid confusion by starting every proportion with a ratio of two *known values,* for example, 15 grains : 1 gram (*known* equivalents), or 5 grains : 1 tablet (dosage in a certain unit of measure which is *known* to be available for administration), or 5% : 100% (*known* strengths of solutions). Next, when using Formulas A and B make certain that the unit of measure of the third term is the same as that in the first term and that the unit of measure of the fourth term is the same as that in the second term. When using Formula C the unit of measure of the first and second terms must be the same, and the third and fourth terms must be in another unit of measure.

Formula A (conversions)	known equivalents
	15 gr. : 1 Gm. = x gr. : 0.5 Gm.
Formula B (dosages)	known to be available for administration
	5 gr. : 1 tablet = 15 gr. : x tablet(s)
Formula C (solutions)	known strengths of solutions
	5% : 100% = x ml. : 1000 ml.

5

As stated above, in all dosage and solutions problems there may be two, but no more than two, different units of measure in addition to numerical values. Label every term in the proportion with a unit of measure. Forget these units of measure when multiplying means and extremes. Finally, label x, the unknown quantity, with the appropriate unit of measure.

Examples:

Problem 1. Determine the gr. equivalent of 0.5 Gm.

Solution with Formula A: known equivalents

$$15 \text{ gr.} : 1 \text{ Gm.} = x \text{ gr.} : 0.5 \text{ Gm.}$$
$$1x = 7\text{-}1/2$$
$$x = 7\text{-}1/2 \text{ gr.}$$

Problem 2. Determine how many tablets to administer when the order is for aspirin gr. xv and the available tablets are gr. v each.

Solution with Formula B: known to be available
                              for administration

$$5 \text{ gr.} : 1 \text{ tablet} = 15 \text{ gr.} : x \text{ tablet(s)}$$
$$5x = 15$$
$$x = 3 \text{ tablets}$$

Problem 3. Determine how much 100% Lysol is needed to make 1 qt. (1000 ml.) of 5% Lysol solution.

Solution with Formula C: known strengths
                              of solutions

$$5\% : 100\% = x \text{ ml.} : 1000 \text{ ml.}$$
$$100x = 5000$$
$$x = 50 \text{ ml. of } 100\% \text{ Lysol}$$

Note that the first ratio or the first and the second terms in the proportion above are all *known* values. All dosage problems can be solved by using Formula B, all solutions problems by using Formula C. By using the few equivalents listed in Table 1 and Formula A, one can determine almost all other equivalents nurses will ever need to know.

DETERMINING EQUIVALENT VALUES

Three examples of determining equivalent values by using Formula A are presented below, along with discussions of commonly encountered problems.

6

Additional help in determining equivalents will be given with the solutions to the various types of dosage and solutions problems to be presented later.

Examples:
Problem 1. 1 gr. = ? mg.

Solution 1:

known equivalents	unknown equivalents

$$15 \text{ gr.} : 1000 \text{ mg.} = 1 \text{ gr.} : x \text{ mg.}$$
$$15x = 1000$$
$$x = 66.67 \text{ mg.}$$

or

Solution 2:

$$16 \text{ gr.} : 1000 \text{ mg.} = 1 \text{ gr.} : x \text{ mg.}$$
$$16x = 1000$$
$$x = 62.5 \text{ mg.}$$

If one remembers the numbers 60, 64, and 65 mg. given in equivalent tables and remembers that 15 or 16 gr. = 1 Gm. = 1000 mg., one can readily see that 1 gr. = 60, 64, or 65 mg. and that 1 mg. = 1/60, 1/64, or 1/65 gr. Any of these values will be accurate enough for calculation of dosages. Often the choice of one over the other two will enable division of numerators and denominators by the same number in order to reduce these parts of fractions to smaller numerical values which are more likely to be the same values as the ordered dosages.

Problem 2. 32 mg. = ? gr.

Solution 1:

$$1 \text{ gr.} : 64 \text{ mg.} = x \text{ gr.} : 32 \text{ mg.}$$
$$64x = 32$$
$$x = 1/2 \text{ gr.}$$

rather than

Solution 2:

$$1 \text{ gr.} : 60 \text{ mg.} = x \text{ gr.} : 32 \text{ mg.}$$
$$60x = 32$$
$$x = 32/60 = 8/15 \text{ gr.}$$

If the physician's order is for 32 mg. of a certain drug and the tablets are labelled in gr., use 1 gr. : 64 mg. = x gr. : 32 mg. If the physician's order is for 30 mg. of this drug, use 1 gr. : 60 mg. = x gr. : 30 mg., because whether the doctor orders 30 mg. or 32 mg. the available tablets will probably be labelled "gr. 1," "gr. 1/2," or "gr. 1/4." Of course, the tablets may be labelled "30 mg.," or "32 mg.," or possibly "0.03 Gm.," "0.032 Gm.," or "0.034 Gm."

Problem 3. Nembutal 100 mg. = Nembutal ? gr.

Solution 1:
$$15 \text{ gr.} : 1000 \text{ mg.} = x \text{ gr.} : 100 \text{ mg.}$$
$$1000x = 1500$$
$$x = 1\text{-}1/2 \text{ gr.}$$

Solution 2:
$$1 \text{ gr.} : 65 \text{ mg.} = x \text{ gr.} : 100 \text{ mg.}$$
$$65x = 100$$
$$x = 1\text{-}35/65 \text{ gr.}$$

Solution 3:
$$1 \text{ gr.} : 60 \text{ mg.} = x \text{ gr.} : 100 \text{ mg.}$$
$$60x = 100$$
$$x = 1\text{-}2/3 \text{ gr.}$$

Solution 4:
$$1 \text{ gr.} : 64 \text{ mg.} = x \text{ gr.} : 100 \text{ mg.}$$
$$64x = 100$$
$$x = 1\text{-}9/16 \text{ gr.}$$

There are a few basic rules which apply to all problems. One is that no more than a 10% margin of difference between ordered and administered dosages may be considered safe. For example, if the physician orders Nembutal 100 mg. no more than 110 mg. or no less than 90 mg. should be administered. This margin of difference allows for variances in determined dosages which may result from the particular equivalent values used. For example, Nembutal may be available in capsules gr. 3/4 and gr. 1-1/2. If gr. 1 = 60 mg., then gr. 1-1/2 = 90 mg., and 1 tablet labelled "gr. 1-1/2" may safely be given. This, and most problems, can be solved many different ways, giving slightly different but accurate answers.

CHAPTER II
ORAL DOSAGES

TABLETS AND CAPSULES

A second general rule for administering ordered dosages of medications is that only scored or marked tablets can be divided accurately; capsules cannot be divided accurately. Therefore, look for tablets or capsules of the desired dosage. Rarely will a physician order a drug in capsule or tablet form which is not available in the dosage ordered. However, ordering fractional dosages of tablets to be dissolved in sterile solution before parenteral administration is one common exception. Examples of this exception, which include orders for atropine sulfate or for scopolamine to be given hypodermically, will be discussed in Chapter III. Hereafter, unless otherwise indicated, all tablets are to be considered as non-scored tablets. Also, unless otherwise indicated (age in parentheses) all examples and practice problems involve the calculation of dosages for adults. Usually one should give the ordered dosage using as few tablets as possible.

Before discussing the calculation of oral tablet and capsule dosages it might be noted that this process frequently is not necessary. Often when oral drugs in tablet or capsule form are ordered, the physician will order the number to be given. Nurses may safely administer the number of tablets or capsules ordered *if* they are certain that the drug ordered is available in one dosage only. For example, an order for "Thorazine tablet 1 t.i.d." cannot be carried out because Thorazine is available in 10, 25, 50, and 200 mg. tablets.

Examples:

Problem 1. *Ordered:* Aspirin 10 gr. q.4h. p.o. p.r.n. for pain.

  Available: Acetylsalicylic acid (aspirin) 5-gr. tablets.

Solution: Formula B

known to be available for administration	ordered dosage

$$5 \text{ gr. : } 1 \text{ tablet} = 10 \text{ gr. : } x \text{ tablet(s)}$$
$$5x = 10$$
$$x = 2 \text{ tablets}$$

  Answer: Administer 2 aspirin tablets 5 gr. each orally every 4 hours when required.

Whenever the available medication is labelled in the same unit of measure as the physician's order only Formula B is needed to solve the problem, as seen above. Both Formula A and Formula B are needed to solve problems in which the available and ordered units of measure differ, as seen below. In such instances note that one may either convert the unit of measure of the tablet available to the same unit of measure as the ordered dosage as in Problem 2, or one may convert the ordered dosage to the same unit of measure as the tablet available as in Problem 3.

Problem 2.   Ordered: Aspirin 10 gr. q.4h. p.o. p.r.n. for temperature
over 102°F.

Available: Acetylsalicylic acid (ASA) 0.3-Gm. tablets.

Solution: Formula A

known equivalents	available for administration
15 gr. : 1 Gm. =	x gr. : 0.3 Gm.
1x =	4.5
x =	4.5 or 5 gr.,
	therefore
	0.3 Gm. equals 5 gr.

Formula B

known to be available for administration	ordered dosage
5 gr. : 1 tablet =	10 gr. : x tablet(s)
5x =	10
x =	2 tablets

Answer: Administer 2 ASA tablets 0.3 Gm. each orally
every 4 hours when required for temperature
over 102°F.

If the equivalent 16 gr. : 1 Gm. had been used above then 0.3 Gm. would equal 4.8 gr. Actually, whenever a tablet is labelled "0.33 Gm." or "0.3 Gm." one may assume that this equals 1/3 Gm. or 5 gr. Conversely, one may assume that a tablet labelled "5 gr." equals 0.33 Gm. or 0.3 Gm. Likewise, 10 gr. equals 0.66 Gm. or 0.6 Gm. Remembering this will eliminate much difficulty when doing dosage problems.

Problem 3.   Ordered: Nembutal 1-1/2 gr. p.o. h.s. p.r.n.

Available: Pentobarbital sodium (Nembutal Sodium) 50-
and 100-mg. capsules.

Solution:	Formula A	known equivalents	ordered dosage

$$1 \text{ gr.} : 60 \text{ mg.} = 1\text{-}1/2 \text{ gr.} : x \text{ mg.}$$
$$1x = 90$$
$$x = 90 \text{ mg.}$$

or

$$1 \text{ gr.} : 64 \text{ mg.} = 1\text{-}1/2 \text{ gr.} : x \text{ mg.}$$
$$1x = 96$$
$$x = 96 \text{ mg.}$$

or

$$15 \text{ gr.} : 1000 \text{ mg.} = 1\text{-}1/2 \text{ gr.} : x \text{ mg.}$$
$$15x = 1500$$
$$x = 100 \text{ mg.}$$

Formula B	known to be available for administration	ordered dosage

$$100 \text{ mg.} : 1 \text{ capsule} = 100 \text{ mg.} : x \text{ capsule(s)}$$
$$100x = 100$$
$$x = 1 \text{ capsule}$$

Answer: Administer 1 Nembutal 100-mg. capsule orally at hour of sleep (bedtime) when required.

Problem 4.   *Ordered:*   Phenobarbital 15 mg. p.o. q.i.d.

Available: Phenobarbital (Luminol) tablets 1/4 gr., 1/2 gr., 1 gr., and 1-1/2 gr.

Solution:

$$60 \text{ mg.} : 1 \text{ gr.} = 15 \text{ mg.} : x \text{ gr.}$$
$$60x = 15$$
$$x = 15/1 \div 60$$
$$x = 15/1 \times 1/60$$
$$x = 1/4 \text{ gr.}$$

Answer: Administer 1 phenobarbital tablet 1/4 gr. orally 4 times a day.

Problem 5.   *Ordered:*   Digoxin 1/120 gr. p.o. q.d.

Available: Digoxin (Lanoxin) tablets 0.25 mg.

Solution:
$$1 \text{ mg. : } 1/60 \text{ gr.} = x \text{ mg. : } 1/120 \text{ gr.}$$
$$1/60x = 1/120$$
$$x = 1/120 \div 1/60 =$$
$$1/120 \times 60/1 =$$
$$60/120 = 1/2$$
$$x = 0.5 \text{ mg.}$$

$$0.25 \text{ mg. : } 1 \text{ tablet} = 0.5 \text{ mg. : } x \text{ tablet(s)}$$
$$0.25x = 0.5$$
$$x = 2 \text{ tablets}$$

Answer: Administer 2 Lanoxin tablets 0.25 mg. orally every day.

Problem 6.   *Ordered:*   Phenergan 0.05 Gm. p.o. stat.

Available: Promethazine hydrochloride (Phenergan HC1) tablets 12.5 mg. and 25 mg.

Solution:
$$1 \text{ Gm. : } 1000 \text{ mg.} = 0.05 \text{ Gm. : } x \text{ mg.}$$
$$1x = 50$$
$$x = 50 \text{ mg.}$$

$$25 \text{ mg. : } 1 \text{ tablet} = 50 \text{ mg. : } x \text{ tablet(s)}$$
$$25x = 50$$
$$x = 2 \text{ tablets}$$

Answer: Administer 2 Phenergan tablets 25 mg. orally immediately.

Practice Problems:

1. *Ordered:*   Equanil 0.2 Gm. p.o. q.i.d.
    Available: Meprobamate (Miltown, Equanil) scored tablets 400 mg.

    Answer: ....

2. *Ordered:*   Chloromycetin 0.5 Gm. p.o. q.6h.
    Available: Chloramphenicol (Chloromycetin) capsules 250 mg.

    Answer: ....

3. *Ordered:*   Prostaphlin 1 Gm. p.o. q.4h.
    Available: Oxacillin (Prostaphlin) tablets 250 mg.

    Answer: ....

4. *Ordered:*   (11-year-old patient) Cortisone 12.5 mg. p.o. q.i.d.
    Available: Cortisone acetate scored tablets 5 mg., 10 mg., and 25 mg.

    Answer: ....

5. *Ordered:*   Cortisone 0.025 Gm. p.o. q.i.d.
   Available: Cortisone acetate scored tablets 5 mg. and 10 mg.

   Answer: ....

6. *Ordered:*   Seconal 1-1/2 gr. p.o. h.s. p.r.n. and may repeat 1 time.
   Available: Secobarbital sodium (Seconal Sodium) capsules 50 mg.

   Answer: ....

7. *Ordered:*   (4-year-old patient) Sulfadiazine 4 gr. p.o. q.i.d.
   Available: Sulfadiazine scored tablets 0.5 Gm.

   Answer: ....

8. *Ordered:*   Sulfadiazine 1.5 Gm. p.o. q.i.d.
   Available: Sulfadiazine scored tablets 500 mg.

   Answer: ....

14

9. *Ordered:*   Neomycin 1 Gm. q.4h. p.o. for 72 hrs. prior to surgery.
   Available: Neomycin sulfate tablets 500 mg.

   Answer: ....

10. *Ordered:*   Phenobarbital 1-1/2 gr. p.o. q.i.d.
    Available: Phenobarbital sodium tablets 32 mg. and 64 mg.

    Answer: ....

11. *Ordered:*   Atropine 0.5 mg. p.o. q.i.d.
    Available: Atropine sulfate tablets 1/200 gr., 1/150 gr., and 1/120 gr.

    Answer: ....

12. *Ordered:*   Dilantin 1-1/2 gr. p.o. t.i.d.
    Available: Dilantin sodium capsules 30 mg. and 100 mg. and scored
                  tablets 50 mg.

    Answer: ....

15

DRUGS IN SOLUTIONS

When oral drugs in solution are ordered the physician frequently will order the volume amount to be given. No calculation of dosage is necessary. Some examples of such orders are as follows:

Elixir Alurate ℥ii p.o. q.3-4h. p.r.n.
Milk of magnesia ℥i stat.
Lugol's solution 5 drops t.i.d.
Terpin hydrate 5 ml. q.4h. p.r.n. for cough.
Gelusil 30 ml. t.i.d. a.c. and h.s.
Robitussin 5 cc. q.2h. p.r.n. for cough.
S.S.K.I. 10 gtts. stat then t.i.d.
Paregoric 5 ml. stat.
Donnatol 5 cc. t.i.d. a.c. and h.s.

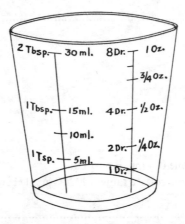

Figure 1. One-ounce medicine glass.

One-ounce receptacles used for administering drugs orally vary but most are marked in drams and milliliters (or cc.) and many also include teaspoon and tablespoon measurements. Therefore, relatively large amounts can be measured quite accurately in one-ounce containers. However, other means must be used to measure smaller units of measure such as minims and drops.

Drops is an approximate, household unit of measurement; minims is an accurate, metric unit of measurement. Therefore, one may safely substitute minims for drops but one should never measure a dosage in drops when minims are ordered. Minim pipettes or syringes may be used to measure minims. Medicine droppers are used to measure drops. The size of drops varies considerably depending upon the viscosity and temperature of the solution, the size of the opening in the dropper, the force with which the solution is expelled, and the angle at which the dropper is held. Holding the dropper at a 45-degree angle is suggested when measuring drugs.

Solutions for parenteral administration also occasionally may be ordered in a volume unit of measure. For example, the physician may order "Bejectal 1 ml. I.M. twice weekly." However, when the physician orders oral or parenteral preparations of drugs in solution he frequently orders a number of milligrams, grams, or other units of weight measure. Nurses must then convert these to drams, ounces, milliliters, or other units of volume measure in order to administer the prescribed dosage.

Labels on drugs in solution may indicate a certain weight measure in a particular volume measure, for example, 500 mg./5 ml. or 10 gr. in 1 dram. Labels on these drugs also may merely state a percentage or a ratio strength of the solutions.

Whenever the strength of a drug which is available in solution is stated as a ratio or as a percentage strength, it must be remembered that the parts are equal parts. A 5% solution therefore may be said to contain 5 Gm. in every 100 ml. because 1 Gm. = 1 ml. It may also be said to contain 5 gr. in every 100 m. because 1 gr. = 1 m. A 1:1000 solution contains 1 gr. in every 1000 m., 1 Gm. in every 1000 ml., 1000 mg. in every 1000 ml., or 1 mg. in every 1 ml. One Gm. of a drug usually does not equal 1 ml., but when administering drugs in solution form we can assume this equality because the pharmacist or pharmaceutical company has weighed, not measured, the drug. There will be 1 Gm. of drug in 1000 ml. of a 1:1000 solution or 1 mg. of drug in 1 ml. of this 1:1000 solution. It does not matter how much of the drug one says is available for administration in the first and second terms of the proportion when calculating the dosage. It is only the strength of the solution available for administration that is important. After determining how much of the solution is needed in order to give the desired dosage one can determine whether or not the vial, ampule, or bottle contains enough solution.

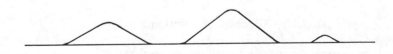

Figure 2. One gram each of three different drugs.

Units of measure other than those found in the metric, apothecaries', or household systems may be used to indicate the quantity of a drug either in oral or parenteral solution. Units, abbreviated U., and milliequivalents, abbreviated mEq., are the most commonly used examples. Occasionally such units of measure are used for drugs in tablet or capsule form. Physicians will order a quantity of milliequivalents or units. Labels on the drugs will indicate the number of milliequivalents or units in a particular volume or capacity measure, for example, 400,000 U. per ml. or 20 mEq. per 15 ml.

A milliequivalent, which is equal to one thousandth of an equivalent, refers to the number of ionic charges of an element or a compound. It is a measure of the chemical combining power of a substance. Potassium chloride (KCl) is an example of a drug ordered in milliequivalents.

Measuring drugs in units means something somewhat different for every drug measured this way. One U.S.P. insulin unit promotes the metabolism of about 1.5 Gm. of dextrose. The penicillin unit is the equivalent of the antibiotic activity of 0.6 mcg. of U.S.P. Penicillin Sodium Reference Standard. One mg. of this kind of penicillin equals 1,667 units. Other kinds of penicillin have different mg. to units equivalents. For example, 1 mg. of benzathine penicillin equals 1,211 U.S.P. units.

Examples:

Problem 1.   *Ordered:*   Chloral hydrate liquid 7-1/2 gr. h.s.

                Available: Chloral hydrate 10 gr. per fluid dram.

Solution: Formula B   know to be available
for administration   ordered dosage

$$10 \text{ gr.} : 4 \text{ ml. (1 fl. dram)} = 7\text{-}1/2 \text{ gr.} : x \text{ ml.}$$
$$10x = 30$$
$$x = 3 \text{ ml.}$$

        Answer: Administer 3 ml. chloral hydrate liquid at bedtime.

Problem 2:   *Ordered:*   Glucose 25 Gm. p.o. t.i.d. today.

                Available: Glucose 50% solution.

Solution: Formula B   known to be available
for administration   ordered dosage

$$50 \text{ Gm.} : 100 \text{ ml.} = 25 \text{ Gm.} : x \text{ ml.}$$
$$50x = 2500$$
$$x = 50 \text{ ml.}$$

        Answer: Administer 50 ml. 50% glucose solution orally
3 times today.

18

Problem 3.	Ordered:	Isotonic sodium chloride (NaCl) 1 Gm. orally q.6h.

Available: Isotonic NaCl (0.9 : 100) solution.

Solution: Formula B   known to be available

for administration	ordered dosage

$$0.9 \text{ Gm.} : 100 \text{ ml.} = 1 \text{ Gm.} : x \text{ ml.}$$
$$0.9x = 100$$
$$x = 100 \div 9/10 =$$
$$100/1 \times 10/9 =$$
$$1000/9 =$$
$$111\text{-}1/9 \text{ ml.}$$

Answer: Administer 111-1/9 ml. isotonic NaCl solution by mouth every 6 hours.

Problem 4.   Ordered: (5-year-old patient) Sulfadiazine suspension 300 mg. q.i.d.

Available: Sulfadiazine suspension 0.25 Gm. per 5 ml.

Solution:

$$1 \text{ Gm.} : 1000 \text{ mg.} = x \text{ Gm.} : 300 \text{ mg.}$$
$$1000x = 300$$
$$x = 0.3 \text{ Gm.}$$

$$0.25 \text{ Gm.} : 5 \text{ ml.} = 0.3 \text{ Gm.} : x \text{ ml.}$$
$$0.25x = 1.5$$
$$x = 6 \text{ ml.}$$
$$\text{or}$$
$$1 \text{ Gm.} : 1000 \text{ mg.} = 0.25 \text{ Gm.} : x \text{ mg.}$$
$$1x = 250$$
$$x = 250 \text{ mg.}$$

$$250 \text{ mg.} : 5 \text{ ml.} = 300 \text{ mg.} : x \text{ ml.}$$
$$250x = 1500$$
$$x = 6 \text{ ml.}$$

Answer: Administer 6 ml. sulfadiazine suspension 4 times a day.

Problem 5.   Ordered: (18-month-old patient) Potassium gluconate 10 mEq. p.o. q.i.d.

Available: Kaon Elixir (potassium gluconate) 20 mEq./15 ml.

Solution:

20 mEq. : 15 ml. = 10 mEq. : x ml.
20x = 150
x = 7.5 ml.

Answer: Administer 7.5 ml. Kaon Elixir orally every 6 hours.

Problem 6.   *Ordered:*   (6-year-old patient) Penicillin G suspension 300,000 U. q.4h.

Available: Benzathine penicillin G oral suspension 150,000 units per 5 ml.

Solution:

150,000 U. : 5 ml. = 300,000 U. : x ml.
150,000x = 1,500,000
x = 10 ml.

Answer: Administer 10 ml. penicillin G suspension every 4 hours.

Practice Problems:

1. *Ordered:*   Paregoric 5 ml. stat.
    Available: Paregoric ℥ii

    Answer: ....

2. *Ordered:*   (4-month-old patient) PAS solution 50 mg. q.i.d.
    Available: Para-aminosalicylic acid (PAS) 0.5 Gm. per 5 cc.

    Answer: ....

3. *Ordered:*   PAS solution 3 Gm. q.i.d.
    Available: Para-aminosalicylic acid (PAS) 0.5 Gm. per 5 cc.

    Answer: ....

4. *Ordered:*   Mycostatin oral suspension 500,000 U. t.i.d.
    Available: Nystatin (Mycostatin) oral suspension 100,000 units per ml.

    Answer: ....

21

5.   *Ordered:*   Magnesium sulfate 10 Gm. p.o. stat.
        Available: Magnesium sulfate 50% solution.

        Answer: ....

6.   *Ordered:*   Paregoric and milk of bismuth ℥ī āā t.i.d.
        Available: Paregoric and milk of bismuth ℥ī āā.

        Answer: ....

7.   *Ordered:*   (20-month-old baby) Ephedrine liquid 3 mg. q.4h. p.r.n.
        Available: Ephedrine sulfate 1/8 gr. per 5 cc.

        Answer: ....

8.   *Ordered:*   (3-year-old patient) Tincture digitoxin 0.02 mg. q.d.
        Available: Tincture digitoxin 100 mcg. per ml.

        Answer: ....

9. *Ordered:*   (8-year-old patient) Gantrisin suspension 0.4 Gm. q.4h.
    Available: Sulfisoxazole (Gantrisin) suspension 100 mg. per ml.

    Answer: ....

10. *Ordered:*   Elixir terpin hydrate with codeine 1/8 gr. q.4h. p.r.n.
                  for cough.
    Available: Terpin hydrate and codeine elixir 2 mg. per ml.

    Answer: ....

11. *Ordered:*   (13-year-old patient) Ilotycin suspension 400 mg. q.6h.
    Available: Erythromycin (Ilotycin) suspension 0.2 Gm. per 5 cc.

    Answer: ....

12. *Ordered:*   Kaon Elixir 20 mEq. t.i.d.
    Available: Potassium gluconate (Kaon) 20 mEq. per 15 ml.

    Answer: ....

CHAPTER III

PARENTERAL DOSAGES

DRUGS IN SOLUTIONS

These problems are solved in exactly the same way as are the oral solutions problems in Chapter II. However, all answers will be in minims and/or milliliters, because this is how syringes are calibrated.

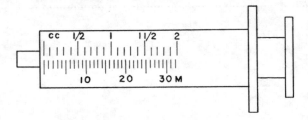

A. A 2-ml. Hypodermic Syringe.

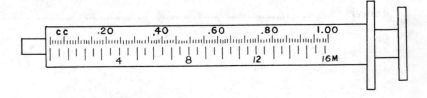

B. Tuberculin Syringe.

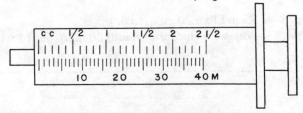

C. A 2.5-ml. Hypodermic Syringe.

Figure 3. Hypodermic and Tuberculin Syringes.

Examples:

Problem 1.   *Ordered:*   Streptomycin 500 mg. b.i.d. I.M.

           Available: Streptomycin sulfate 1 Gm. in 2 ml.

Solution:

$$1 \text{ Gm.} : 1000 \text{ mg.} = x \text{ Gm.} : 500 \text{ mg.}$$
$$1000x = 500$$
$$x = 0.5 \text{ Gm.}$$

$$1 \text{ Gm.} : 2 \text{ ml.} = 0.5 \text{ Gm.} : x \text{ ml.}$$
$$1x = 1$$
$$x = 1 \text{ ml.}$$

           Answer: Administer 1 ml. streptomycin sulfate (1 Gm. in 2 ml.) intramuscularly twice daily.

Problem 2.   *Ordered:*   Codeine 30 mg. s.c. q.4h. p.r.n. for pain.

           Available: 20-ml. vial codeine sulfate labelled "1 gr. in 1 ml."

Solution:

$$60 \text{ mg.} : 1 \text{ gr.} = 30 \text{ mg.} : x \text{ gr.}$$
$$60x = 30$$
$$x = 1/2 \text{ gr.}$$

$$1 \text{ gr.} : 1 \text{ ml.} = 1/2 \text{ gr.} : x \text{ ml.}$$
$$1x = 1/2$$
$$x = 0.5 \text{ ml.}$$

           Answer: Administer 0.5 ml. codeine sulfate subcutaneously every 4 hours when required for pain.

Problem 3.   *Ordered:*   Adrenalin 0.4 mg. "H" q.3h. p.r.n. for asthma.

           Available: 1-ml. ampules epinephrine (Adrenalin) 1:1000 (1 Gm. : 1000 ml. or 1 gr. : 1000 m.).

Solution:

1 Gm. : 1000 ml. <u>or</u>
1000 mg. : 1000 ml. <u>or</u> 1 mg. : 1 ml.

$$1 \text{ mg.} : 1 \text{ ml.} = 0.4 \text{ mg.} : x \text{ ml.}$$
$$1x = 0.4$$
$$x = 0.4 \text{ ml.}$$

           Answer: Administer 0.4 ml. epinephrine 1:1000 subcutaneously or intramuscularly every 3 hours when required.

Problem 4.   *Ordered:*   Levo-Dromoran 1.5 mg. s.c. q.6h. p.r.n. for pain.

Available: Levorphanol tartrate (Levo-Dromoran) 1-ml. ampules labelled "2 mg. per ml."

Solution:

$$2 \text{ mg.} : 16 \text{ m.} (1 \text{ ml.}) = 1.5 \text{ mg.} : x \text{ m.}$$
$$2x = 24$$
$$x = 12 \text{ m.}$$

Answer: Administer 12 m. Levo-Dromoran subcutaneously every 6 hours as needed for pain.

Note that 16 m. was used as the equivalent of 1 ml.; therefore, 2 ml. equals 32 m. Whenever drugs are given with a hypodermic or tuberculin syringe, use 16 m. = 1 ml. rather than 15 m. = 1 ml. when calculating the amount to be given. This gives one a more accurate answer because these syringes are calibrated either with 16 m. per ml. or 16 plus m. per ml., not with 15 m. per ml. Hypodermic syringes are calibrated in tenths of ml. also. In order to give 1.25 ml. one would fill the syringe to the point one-half way between 1.2 and 1.3 ml. To give 1.33 ml. fill the syringe to the point as nearly one-third of the way between 1.3 and 1.4 ml. as possible. Tuberculin syringes are calibrated in hundredths of ml. as well as in minims. When measuring small amounts of parenteral solutions, for example, 2 m. or 0.125 ml., use of a tuberculin syringe is desirable.

Problem 5.   *Ordered:*   Procaine penicillin 400,000 U. I.M. b.i.d.

Available: 10-ml. vial procaine penicillin G 300,000 U. per ml.

Solution:

$$300,000 \text{ U.} : 1 \text{ ml.} = 400,000 \text{ U.} : x \text{ ml.}$$
$$300,000x = 400,000$$
$$3x = 4$$
$$x = 1.33 \text{ ml.}$$

Answer: Administer 1.33 ml. procaine penicillin G intramuscularly twice a day.

Problem 6.   *Ordered:*   Calcium gluconate 1 Gm. I.V. stat.

Available: 10-ml. ampule calcium gluconate 10% (10 Gm. : 100 ml.)

Solution:

$$10 \text{ Gm.} : 100 \text{ ml.} = 1 \text{ Gm.} : x \text{ ml.}$$
$$10x = 100$$
$$x = 10 \text{ ml.}$$

Answer: Administer 10 ml. of 10% calcium gluconate intravenously immediately. (Nurse will prepare; physician will administer.)

Practice Problems:

1. *Ordered:*   ACTH gel 40 U. I.M. q.12h.
   Available: 5-ml. vials corticotropin injection (Acthar Gel) 20 units per ml. and 80 units per ml.

   Answer: ....

2. *Ordered:*   Cedilanid-D 0.6 mg. I.M. q.d.
   Available: 2-ml. and 4-ml. ampules of desacetyl-lanatoside C (Cedilanid-D) containing 0.4 mg. and 0.8 mg. respectively.

   Answer: ....

3. *Ordered:*   (1-year-old patient) Cedilanid-D 0.025 mg. I.M. q.d.
   Available: 2-ml. and 4-ml. ampules desacetyl-lanatoside C (Cedilanid-D) containing 0.4 mg. and 0.8 mg. respectively.

   Answer: ....

4. *Ordered:*   Konakion 20 mg. I.M. q.d.
   Available: 2-1/2 cc. ampule containing Konakion (vitamin K_1) 25 mg.

   Answer: ....

5. *Ordered:* Demerol 75 mg. "H" q.4h. p.r.n. pain
   Available: 30-cc. vial Demerol (meperidine hydrochloride) containing 50 mg. per cc.

   Answer: ....

6. *Ordered:* Hypaque 50 mg. intradermally at 9 a.m. tomorrow.
   Available: 1-cc. ampules 50% Hypaque sodium solution.

   Answer: ....

7. *Ordered:* Reserpine 5 mg. I.M. stat.
   Available: 2-ml. ampules containing Serpasil (reserpine) 2.5 mg. per ml.

   Answer: ....

8. *Ordered:* Procaine penicillin 500,000 U. I.M. b.i.d.
   Available: 10-cc. vial Wycillin (procaine penicillin G in aqueous suspension) 300,000 units per cc.

   Answer: ....

9. *Ordered:* Adrenalin 0.5 mg. "H" q.3h. p.r.n. for asthma.
   Available: 30-ml. vial epinephrine (Adrenalin) 1:2000.

   Answer: ....

10. *Ordered:* Tigan 200 mg. I.M. stat. then 100 mg. q.6h. p.r.n. nausea.
    Available: 20-ml. vial and 2-ml. ampules trimethobenzamide hydro-
    chloride (Tigan HC1) 100 mg. per ml.
    Answer: ....

11. *Ordered:* Aminophylline 0.5 Gm. I.M. q.i.d. p.r.n. for asthma.
    Available: 2-cc. ampule containing Aminophylline 500 mg. (7-1/2 gr.).

    Answer: ....

12. *Ordered:* (2-year-old patient) M.S. 2 mg. "H" pre-op at 10 a.m.
    Available: 30-ml. vial morphine sulfate 16.2 mg. (1/4 gr.) per ml.

    Answer: ....

TABLETS

Many drugs are now available in solution which once were available only in tablet form. Unfortunately, dissolving tablets in sterile solutions for parenteral administration is still necessary at times. Sometimes one must give a fractional part of one or two tablets in order to administer the ordered dosage. Such instances illustrate the exception, cited earlier, to the rule of not dividing non-scored tablets.

Examples:

Problem 1. *Ordered:* Atropine 1/150 gr. "H" pre-op at 9 a.m. tomorrow.

Available: Atropine sulfate hypodermic tablets 1/200, 1/150, 1/120, 1/100, and 1/50 gr.

Answer: Dissolve 1 atropine sulfate hypodermic tablet 1/150 gr. in 1 ml. diluent or solvent (sterile N.S. or sterile D.W.) in a hypodermic syringe and administer subcutaneously at 9 a.m. tomorrow.

Problem 2. *Ordered:* Atropine 1/100 gr. "H" pre-op at noon today.

Available: Atropine sulfate tablets 1/200 gr.

Solution:

$$1/200 \text{ gr.} : 1 \text{ tablet} = 1/100 \text{ gr.} : x \text{ tablet(s)}$$
$$1/200x = 1/100$$
$$x = 2 \text{ tablets}$$

Answer: Dissolve 2 atropine sulfate tablets 1/200 gr. each in 20 m. solvent and administer subcutaneously at noon today.

Problem 3. *Ordered:* Atropine 0.3 mg. "H" at 10 a.m.

Available: Atropine sulfate tablets 1/100 gr.

Solution:

$$1 \text{ mg.} : 1/60 \text{ gr.} = 0.3 \text{ mg.} : x \text{ gr.}$$
$$1x = 1/60 \times 3/10 =$$
$$3/600 = 1/200$$
$$x = 1/200 \text{ gr.}$$

30

$$1/100 \text{ gr. : 1 tablet} = 1/200 \text{ gr. : x tablet(s)}$$
$$1/100x = 1/200$$
$$x = 1/2 \text{ tablet}$$

Answer: Dissolve 1 atropine sulfate tablet 1/100 gr. in 20 m. solvent, expel 10 m. and administer the remaining 10 m. subcutaneously at 10 a.m.

After the fraction of the tablet to be given is determined, one must determine the volume of solvent in which to dissolve the tablet. If one chooses an amount, in minims, which is a multiple of the denominator of the fraction to be given, one can more easily determine the part of the solvent which contains the desired dose. For example, one could withdraw 20 minims of sterile normal saline or sterile distilled water into a sterile 2-ml. (32 minims) hypodermic syringe. Either before or after the solvent is obtained, depending upon the method used, place one of the 1/100 gr. atropine tablets in the syringe. After the tablet is completely dissolved in 20 minims of the solvent, expel 10 minims of the solution and administer the remaining 10 minims to the patient. This 10 minims will contain 0.3 mg. (grain 1/200) atropine or the ordered dose. One could also dissolve one of these tablets in 22 minims and give 11 minims or use 24 minims solvent and administer 12 minims.

When possible, the volume of solvent should be kept within the range of 10 to 24 minims. Depending upon the drug, one tablet may not dissolve readily in less than 10 minims. Therefore, at least 10 minims solvent should be used to dissolve one tablet and about 20 minims should be used to dissolve two tablets. Too, when giving all, or a fraction, of the total solvent, there should be at least 10 minims of solution left for administration of the patient. If one drop of 10 minims is lost the patient will receive 9/10 of the ordered dose. If one drop of five minims were to be lost the patient would receive only 8/10 or 4/5 of the ordered dose.

The maximum amount of solvent used should not exceed 24 minims if possible. If one uses more than this amount there is too little space left in a 2-ml. syringe for withdrawing the plunger enough to permit agitation of the solvent and tablet. Also, administering larger than necessary amounts of solution increases the tissue trauma. Examples of some suggested desirable volumes of solvent to be used for dissolving tablets to get various dosages are as follows:

To give 1 tablet:

Dissolve 1 tablet in 10 minims and give 10 minims.
Dissolve 1 tablet in 16 minims and give 16 minims.

To give 2 tablets:

Dissolve 2 tablets in 16 minims and give 16 minims.
Dissolve 2 tablets in 18 minims and give 18 minims.
Dissolve 2 tablets in 20 minims and give 20 minims.

To give 2/3 tablet:

Dissolve 1 tablet in 15 minims and give 10 minims.
Dissolve 1 tablet in 18 minims and give 12 minims.
Dissolve 1 tablet in 21 minims and give 14 minims.
Dissolve 1 tablet in 24 minims and give 16 minims.

To give 1-1/3 tablets:

$$1\text{-}1/3 \text{ tablets} = \frac{1\text{-}1/3 \text{ tablets}}{2 \text{ tablets}} = 4/3 \div 2/1 = 4/3 \times 1/2 = 4/6 = 2/3$$

or

1-1/3 tablets = 2/3 of 2 tablets

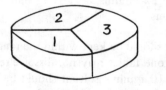 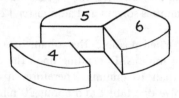

Figure 4. One and one-third tablets equals 4/6 or 2/3 of 2 tablets.

Dissolve 2 tablets in 18 minims and give 12 minims.
Dissolve 2 tablets in 21 minims and give 14 minims.
Dissolve 2 tablets in 24 minims and give 16 minims.

In summary, solving dosage problems to give tablets parenterally may require as many as three steps. It may be necessary first to convert ordered and available dosages to the same unit of measure. Determining the amount of available tablets to be given will then be the second step. Sometimes the additional step of reducing improper fractions, as shown above, may be necessary if a fraction of two tablets is to be administered.

Problem 4.   Ordered: (4-year-old child) Scopolamine 0.1 mg. "H" at 10 a.m.

| | *Available:* | Scopolamine (hyoscine) hydrobromide tablets 0.6 mg. |

Solution:

$$0.6 \text{ mg.} : 1 \text{ tablet} = 0.1 \text{ mg.} : x \text{ tablet(s)}$$
$$0.6x = 0.1$$
$$x = 1/6 \text{ tablet}$$

Answer: Dissolve 1 scopolamine hydrobromide tablet 0.6 mg. in 24 m. diluent, expel all except 4 m., add 6 m. diluent (in order to have at least 10 m. solution), and administer this solution subcutaneously at 10 a.m.

Problem 5. *Ordered:* Atropine 0.5 mg. "H" as pre-op at 9 a.m.

Available: Atropine sulfate tablets 0.3 mg.

Solution:

$$0.3 \text{ mg.} : 1 \text{ tablet} = 0.5 \text{ mg.} : x \text{ tablet(s)}$$
$$0.3x = 0.5$$
$$x = 5/10 \div 3/10 =$$
$$5/10 \times 10/3 =$$
$$5/3 = 1\text{-}2/3$$
$$x = 1\text{-}2/3 \text{ tablets}$$

$$\frac{1\text{-}2/3 \text{ tablets}}{2 \text{ tablets}} = \frac{5/3}{2} = 5/3 \div 2/1 = 5/3 \times 1/2 = 5/6 \text{ of 2 tablets}$$

Answer: Dissolve 2 atropine sulfate tablets 0.3 mg. in 24 m. diluent, expel 4 m., and administer the remaining 20 m. subcutaneously at 9 a.m.

Problem 6. *Ordered:* Pantopon 15 mg. s.c. q.4h. p.r.n. for pain.

Available: Pantopon tablets 1/3 gr.

Solution:

$$65 \text{ mg.} : 1 \text{ gr.} = x \text{ mg.} : 1/3 \text{ gr.}$$
$$1x = 21\text{-}2/3 \text{ mg.}$$

33

or

64 mg. : 1 gr. = x mg. : 1/3 gr.
1x   = 21-1/3 mg.

or

60 mg. : 1 gr. = x mg. : 1/3 gr.
1x   = 20 mg.

20 mg. : 1 tablet = 15 mg. : x tablet(s)
20x = 15
x = 3/4 tablet

Answer: Dissolve 1 Pantopon tablet 1/3 gr. in 20 m. diluent, expel 5 m., and administer the remaining 15 m. solution subcutaneously every 4 hours when required for pain.

Practice Problems

1. *Ordered:*   Pantopon 1/4 gr. s.c. q.3h. p.r.n. for pain.
   Available: Pantopon hypodermic tablets 20 mg.

   Answer: ....

2. *Ordered:*   Dilaudid 2.5 mg. "H" q.3h. p.r.n. for pain.
   Available: Dilaudid hydrochloride soluble tablets 1 mg., 2 mg., 3 mg., and 4 mg. for parenteral use.

   Answer: ....

3. *Ordered:*   Codeine 40 mg. "H" q.3h. p.r.n. for pain.
   Available: Codeine sulfate hypodermic tablets 1/2 gr. and 1 gr.

   Answer: ....

4. *Ordered:*   (6-year-old patient) M.S. 4 mg. q.4h. p.r.n. for pain.
   Available: Morphine sulfate hypodermic tablets 1/4 gr.

   Answer: ....

5. *Ordered:*   M.S. 16 mg. q.4h. p.r.n. for pain.
    Available: Morphine sulfate hypodermic tablets 1/4 gr.

    Answer: ....

6. *Ordered:*   Demerol 100 mg. and atropine 0.4 mg. pre-op "H" at
                 10 a.m.
    Available: 2-ml. ampules of meperidine hydrochloride (Demerol) 50 mg.
                 per ml. and atropine hypodermic tablets 1/100 gr., 1/150 gr.,
                 and 1/200 gr.

    Answer: ....

7. *Ordered:*   Demerol 75 mg. and scopolamine 0.3 mg. "H" stat.
    Available: 2-ml. ampules of meperidine hydrochloride (Demerol) 50 mg.
                 per ml. and scopolamine hypodermic tablets 1/100 gr.,
                 1/150 gr., and 1/200 gr.

    Answer: ....

8. *Ordered:*   Demerol 75 mg. and scopolamine 0.3 mg. "H" stat.
    Available: 2-ml. ampules of Demerol 50 mg. per ml. and scopolamine
                 hypodermic tablets 1/150 gr. (0.4 mg.) and 1/100 gr. (0.6 mg.)

    Answer: ....

36

9. *Ordered:* (1-year-old child) Atropine 0.1 mg. "H" stat.
   Available: Atropine hypodermic tablets (H.T.) 0.0003 Gm., 0.0004 Gm. and 0.0006 Gm.

   Answer:...

10. *Ordered:* (8-year-old patient) Demerol 30 mg. and scopolamine 0.12 mg. "H" on call.
    Available: 2-ml. ampules of Demerol 50 mg. per ml. and scopolamine H.T. 0.0004 Gm.

    Answer:...

11. *Ordered:* (5-year-old patient) M.S. 2 mg. "H" q.4h. p.r.n.
    Available: Morphine sulfate H.T. 1/4 gr. (15 mg.), 1/6 gr. (10 mg.) and 1/8 gr. (8 mg.)

    Answer: ....

12. *Ordered:* M.S. 1/4 gr. "H" stat.
    Available: Morphine sulfate H.T. 1/8 gr. (8 mg.)

    Answer:...

DRUGS REQUIRING RECONSTITUTION

Some penicillins, other antibiotics, and other drugs to be given parenterally are stored in the crystal or powder form in sterile vials or ampules. Before these drugs are administered they must be dissolved in a desirable diluent or solvent, usually sterile isotonic saline or sterile distilled water. A sterile syringe is used to withdraw the diluent from one vial and to add it to the vial or ampule containing the drug in its dried form. After the drug has been dissolved in this diluent, the correct volume will be administered to the patient. If the entire amount of drug in the vial is to be given at one time, one adds enough diluent to dissolve the drug, usually at least 1 to 2 ml. The amount needed to dissolve the drug will vary with the type and amount of drug in the vial or ampule. Directions for dissolving drugs for parenteral administration usually can be found on the vial, on the box containing the vial, or on a pamphlet in the accompanying box. In some manner these directions will indicate the amount of volume which the drug itself occupies *after* it is in solution. For example, directions may say that adding 1.2 ml. sterile distilled water will yield 2 ml. of reconstituted solution. In other words, although the drug itself occupies considerably less space when in solution than when in the dry form, this particular drug still displaces 0.8 ml. in volume measurement. In order to get a 5-ml. total amount of solution in this particular vial one would add 4.2 ml. diluent. If one added 5 ml. diluent there would be 5.8 ml. in the vial.

Looking to Problem 1 below it can be seen that the total volume of solution after reconstitution should be 10 ml. in order to give the desired or ordered dose of 300,000 units in 1 ml. Therefore, if directions accompanying this vial said that adding 1.5 ml. diluent gives 2 ml. reconstituted solution, one should add 9.5 ml. diluent.

In solving problems such as these the first term of the proportion will be the dosage ordered by the doctor. Ordinarily, one attempts to have the ordered dosage available in 1 ml.; therefore, we who dissolve the drug choose 1 ml. as the second term. The third term is the total amount of drug in the vial. The fourth or unknown term is the total volume desired. This amount is determined first. Then the amount of displacement by the drug is subtracted in order to determine exactly how much diluent to add.

Occasionally the calculated total volume desired will be more than the vial will hold. In such instances, first try halving the calculated total volume of diluent. This will make the desired single dose available in 0.5 ml. instead of 1.0 ml. If, as in Problem 2 below, a 5-ml. vial containing 3,000,000 U. penicillin were available and the doctor ordered 300,000 U. I.M. q. 4h., one could add 4.5 ml. diluent to yield a total volume of 5 ml. Then every 0.5 ml. would contain the ordered dosage of 300,000 U.

Whenever only a portion of the drug in a vial or ampule is used, the container should be properly labelled so that the remaining drug may be given later. Because the ordered dosage is usually prepared to be available in 1 ml., it is a safety precaution to label vials with the dosage per ml., for example, "200,000 U./ml.," or 0.5 Gm./ml.," even though the ordered dosage may be less than the amount of drug in 1 ml. Most drugs should be refrigerated after reconstitution. Placing the date on the labels safeguards against use after suggested expiration times.

In summary, all dosage problems and parenteral solutions problems can be solved with the proportion Formula B, starting with what is known to be available for administration. It may be necessary to use Formula A first, however, if the ordered and available dosages are not in the same unit of measure.

Examples:

Problem 1. *Ordered:* Potassium penicillin G 300,000 U. I.M. q.4h.

Available: A 10-ml. vial containing 3,000,000 units of potassium penicillin G in dry form. Adding 4.5 ml. diluent yields 5 ml. reconstituted solution. (The drug displacement is 5 ml. minus 4.5 ml. or 0.5 ml.)

Solution:

to be made available for administration	total dosage in vial	total vol. of solu.
300,000 U. : 1 ml.	= 3,000,000 U. : x ml.	
300,000x	= 3,000,000	
x	= 10 ml.	
	−0.5 ml.	
	9.5 ml.	

Answer: Add 9.5 ml. of sterile diluent (D.W. or N.S.), label the vial "300,000 U./ml.," and administer 1 ml. intramuscularly every 4 hours.

Problem 2. *Ordered:* Crystalline penicillin 400,000 U. I.M. q.3h.

Available: A 10-ml. vial containing 1,000,000 units of potassium penicillin G in powder form. Adding 1.6 ml. diluent yields 2 ml. reconstituted solution. (The drug displacement is 0.4 ml.)

Solution:

to be made available for administration	total dosage in vial	total vol. of solu.
400,000 U. : 1 ml.	= 1,000,000 U. : x ml.	
400,000x	= 1,000,000	
4x	= 10	
x	= 2.5 ml.	

| *Answer:* | Add 2.1 ml. sterile diluent to vial, label vial "400,000 U./ml.," and administer 1 ml. intramuscularly every 3 hours. (When giving the third dose one will need to reconstitute another vial of penicillin, using the remaining 0.5 ml. from the first vial and adding 0.5 ml. from the second vial.) |

Problem 3. **Ordered:** (10-lb. infant) Staphcillin 125 mg. I.M. q.i.d.

Available: A 5-ml. vial containing 1 Gm. methicillin sodium (Staphcillin) in powder form. Adding 1.5 ml. diluent will yield 2 ml. reconstituted solution.

Solution:

$$125 \text{ mg.} : 1 \text{ ml.} = 1000 \text{ mg.} : x \text{ ml.}$$
$$125x = 100$$
$$x = 8 \text{ ml.}$$

$$\text{and}$$
$$8 \text{ ml.} \div 2 = 4 \text{ ml.}$$
$$4 \text{ ml.} - 0.5 \text{ ml.} = 3.5 \text{ ml.}$$

Answer: This 5-ml. vial will not hold 8 ml. Therefore, prepare one-half as much total solution which will be twice as strong, or prepare 4 ml. by adding 3.5 ml. sterile diluent. Label the vial "250 mg./ml." and administer 0.5 ml. intramuscularly 4 times a day in order to give the 125 mg. ordered.

Problem 4. **Ordered:** Phenobarbital 100 mg. I.M. stat.

Available: 2-ml. ampules of phenobarbital sodium (Sodium Luminal) containing 2 gr. in powder form and 2-ml. ampules containing 5 gr. of drug.

Solution:

$$15 \text{ gr.} : 1000 \text{ mg.} = x \text{ gr.} : 100 \text{ mg.}$$
$$1000x = 1500$$
$$x = 1.5 \text{ gr.}$$
$$\frac{1.5 \text{ gr. ordered}}{2 \text{ gr. available}} = 3/4 \text{ of } 2 \text{ gr.}$$

40

Answer:		Dissolve the 2 gr. of Sodium Luminal (do not confuse with Luminal which cannot be given parenterally) in 24 minims of sterile D.W., expel 6 m. and administer 18 m. of the reconstituted solution intramuscularly immediately, provided the displacement by the drug does not exceed 10% of the ordered dosage, since there is no information about displacement. If adding 24 m. yields more than 26.4 m. (24 m. +10% of 24 m.) note the total amount of solution prepared and administer 3/4 of this amount.

Problem 5.	*Ordered:*	Strep-Dicrysticin 1 cc. q.12h. I.M.
	Available:	A 5-ml. vial of streptomycin 0.5 Gm. and penicillin 400,000 U. (Strep-Dicrysticin) in powder form. Directions say, "Usual dose 2 cc. Add 1.5 cc. diluent." (This means displacement is 0.5 cc.)
	Answer:	Add 1.5 ml. sterile diluent to this vial and dissolve the drug. Label the vial "250 mg. streptomycin and 200,000 U. penicillin/ml." and administer 1 ml. intramuscularly every 12 hours. (One would need to make certain that the physician wants one-half of the "usual dose" of 2 cc. or one-half of the drug in the vial administered every 12 hours.)

| *Problem 6.* | *Ordered:* | Chloromycetin 500 mg. I.M. q.8h. |
| | *Available:* | A 5-ml. vial of chloramphenicol (Chloromycetin Sodium Succinate) 1 Gm. in dry or powder form. Directions on the drug box are as follows: |

Concentration	Diluent
400 mg./cc.	2 cc.
250 mg./cc.	3.8 cc.
100 mg./cc.	11 cc.

> *Answer:* Add 2 ml. sterile diluent to this vial. (The ordered dosage will be available in a little more than 1 ml.) Measure the amount of reconstituted solution, return one-half of the reconstituted solution to the vial and label the vial with one-half the total amount measured as containing 500 mg. Chloromycetin. Administer the other one-half of the solution. There is no way to determine accurately the amount of displacement by this drug because the directions very obviously are wrong, as follows:

Directions with drug:

Concentration	Diluent	Desired Total cc.	Displacement
400 mg./cc.	2 cc.	400 mg. : 1 cc. = 1000 mg. : x cc. x = 2.5 cc.	.5 cc. <u>or</u> 2.5 cc. − 2 cc.
250 mg./cc.	3.8 cc.	250 mg. : 1 cc. = 1000 mg. : x cc. x = 4 cc.	.2 cc. <u>or</u> 4 cc. − 3.8 cc.
100 mg./cc.	11 cc.	100 mg. : 1 cc. = 1000 mg. : x cc. x = 10 cc.	\−1 cc. <u>or</u> 10 cc. − 11 cc.

Displacement by the drug will always be the same no matter how much diluent is added, provided enough diluent is added to dissolve the drug. In this example, the amount of displacement by the drug is not consistent; therefore, the directions with the drug cannot be correct. There is no way of knowing which, if any, of the calculated amounts of displacement may be correct.

It is obvious, therefore, that nurses must watch not only for their own, pharmacist's, and physician's errors but also for those made by pharmaceutical companies.

The following directions on a vial containing 1,000,000 U. of buffered potassium penicillin G show an example of consistent displacement.

To get 100,000 U./ml., add 9.6 ml. diluent (10 ml. − 9.6 ml. = 0.4 ml.)
To get 200,000 U./ml., add 4.6 ml. diluent (5 ml. − 4.6 ml. = 0.4 ml.)
To get 250,000 U./ml., add 3.6 ml. diluent (4 ml. − 3.6 ml. = 0.4 ml.)

In summary, the steps in reconstitution of drugs are listed below.

1. Determine the total amount of reconstituted solution desired in order to give the ordered dosage of drug in 1 ml. if possible.
2. Will the vial or ampule hold this amount?
   A. If so, subtract the amount of displacement from this total amount to determine the amount of diluent to add.

B. If not, will the vial or ampule hold one-half this desired total amount?

    1) If so, divide the desired total amount by 2, then subtract the amount of displacement from the newly determined total amount of solution in order to determine the amount of diluent needed.

        a) Each ml. will contain twice the ordered dosage.

        b) One will administer 0.5 ml. in order to give the ordered dosage.

    2) If not, one may have to prepare, for example, one-third or one-fourth the calculated desired total amount. Divide the desired total amount by 3 or 4 before subtracting the amount of diluent needed.

        a) Each ml. will contain 3 or 4 times the ordered dosage.

        b) One will administer 0.33 or 0.25 ml. in order to give the ordered dosage.

C. If the amount of drug displacement is not given, add a reasonable amount of diluent, dissolve the drug, then draw all the solution into the syringe, and measure the total amount of reconstituted solution; then, determine and administer the proper portion of this total amount in order to give the ordered dosage.

3. Discard unused drug in ampules. Label vials containing unused drug with the amount of drug in each ml. and refrigerate if indicated.

Practice Problems:

1. *Ordered:*   Crystalline penicillin 300,000 U. I.M. q.4h.
   Available: A 20-ml. vial containing 3,000,000 units of potassium penicillin G in dry form. Adding 9.6 ml. diluent yields 10 ml. reconstituted solution.

   Answer: ....

2. *Ordered:*   (4-year-old patient) Aqueous penicillin 200,000 U. I.M. q.3h.
   Available: A 20-ml. vial containing 3,000,000 units of potassium penicillin G in dry form. To get 250,000 U./ml. add 10.6 ml. solvent.

   Answer: ....

3. *Ordered:*   Aqueous ACTH 4 U. I.M. today.
   Available: A 5-ml. vial containing 40 units of corticotropin (ACTH). Directions are to add enough diluent to dissolve.

   Answer: ....

4. *Ordered:*   Dilantin 200 mg. I.M. stat.
   Available: A 10-ml. vial containing sodium diphenylhydantoin (Dilantin) 250 mg. Adding 5.2 cc. of accompanying solvent yields 50 mg./cc. (This vial obviously contains more than 250 mg. of drug.)

   Answer: ....

5. *Ordered:*   Polycillin N 400 mg. I.M. q.6h.
    Available: 5-ml. vials of ampicillin (Polycillin) containing 1 Gm., 500 mg., 250 mg., or 125 mg. of drug in dry form. Directions with 500-mg. vial say to add at least 1.2 ml. diluent. This drug must be used within 1 hr. after reconstitution.

    Answer: ....

6. *Ordered:*   Staphcillin 1 Gm. I.M. q.4h.
    Available: 10-ml. vials of sodium methicillin (Staphcillin) containing 4 Gm. drug in dry form. Adding 5.7 ml. diluent yields 500 mg./ml.

    Answer: ....

7. *Ordered:*   Prostaphlin 500 mg. I.M. q.6h.
    Available: 10-ml. vials of sodium oxacillin (Prostaphlin) 1 Gm. in dry form. If one adds 5.7 ml. D.W. every 1.5 ml. will contain 250 mg.

    Answer: ....

8. *Ordered:*   (1-month-old baby) Keflin 100 mg. I.M. q.6h.
    Available: 10-ml. vials containing sodium cephalothin (Keflin) 1 Gm. in dry form. Adding 4 ml. D.W. yields two 0.5-Gm. doses of 2.2 cc. each. Drug will not go into solution if less than 4 ml. is used.

    Answer: ....

9. *Ordered:* (8-year-old patient) Keflin 300 mg. I.M. q.6h.
   Available: Same as in Problem 8.

   Answer: ....

10. *Ordered:* Coly-mycin 75 mg. I.M. stat and q.12h.
    Available: 5-ml. vials of sodium colistimethate (Coly-mycin) 150 mg.
    Directions are to dissolve in 2 ml. D.W.

    Answer: ....

11. *Ordered:* Phenobarbital 3 gr. I.M. q.h.s.
    Available: 1.5-ml. vials containing phenobarbital sodium 325 mg.
    (5 gr.) in dry form.

    Answer: ....

12. *Ordered:* Crystalline penicillin 400,000 U. I.M. q.3h.
    Available: A 20-ml. vial containing 1,000,000 units of potassium
    penicillin G in dry form. Adding 3.6 ml. diluent yields
    250,000 U./ml.

    Answer: ....

46

INSULIN

There are different kinds of insulin such as regular, N.P.H., and P.Z.I. All kinds of insulin are prepared in various concentrations. The most commonly available strengths are 40 units per ml. (U. 40) or 80 units per ml. (U. 80). Usually insulin is given with insulin syringes which are calibrated for units per ml. (see illustrations below). If the concentration of the insulin being used corresponds with the units per ml. on the syringe scale the correct dosage of insulin can be measured directly. For example, in order to administer 30 units of U. 40 insulin one would fill a U. 40/ml. insulin syringe to the 30-unit mark. Or, to give 60 units of U. 80 insulin, one would fill a U. 80/ml. insulin syringe to the 60-unit mark.

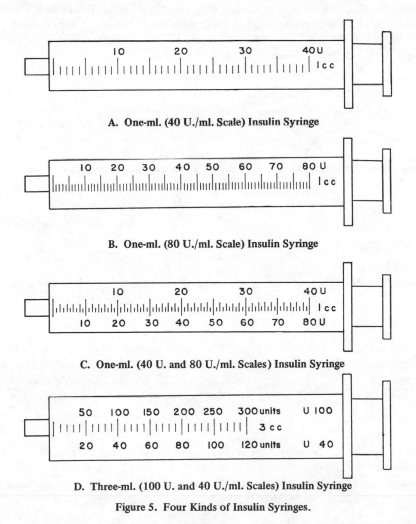

A. One-ml. (40 U./ml. Scale) Insulin Syringe

B. One-ml. (80 U./ml. Scale) Insulin Syringe

C. One-ml. (40 U. and 80 U./ml. Scales) Insulin Syringe

D. Three-ml. (100 U. and 40 U./ml. Scales) Insulin Syringe

Figure 5. Four Kinds of Insulin Syringes.

47

Great caution should be exercised if one attempts to use an insulin syringe when its scale does not correspond with the strength of the insulin being used. For example, if, as in Illustration A above, one has only a 40 U. per ml. syringe and has only U. 80 strength insulin available and 20 units are ordered, one would fill the syringe to the 10-unit mark. Filling the syringe to the 20-unit or to the 40-unit mark is an error so easily committed that one should check and double check before administration. Some institutions require that all insulin dosages be checked by another person. This practice is recommended, especially during initial student experiences.

One might more safely use a hypodermic or a tuberculin syringe when the concentration of the available insulin and the scale on the available insulin syringes do not correspond. When insulin syringes are not available or when the amount of insulin to be given exceeds the capacity of the available insulin syringes, either a hypodermic or a tuberculin syringe may be used. With the use of these syringes one must calculate the ordered insulin dosages in minims or in tenths or hundredths of milliliters, as shown below.

Examples:

Problem 1.   *Ordered:*   Regular insulin 100 U. deep s.c. stat.
                 Available: Regular insulin U. 80 and no insulin syringe.

Solution: Formula B   known to be available
                                          for administration   ordered dosage

$$U.\ 80 : 1\ ml. \ = \ U.\ 100 : x\ ml.$$
$$80x \ = \ 100$$
$$x \ = \ 1.25\ ml.$$

or

$$U.\ 80 : 16\ m. \ = \ U.\ 100 : x\ m.$$
$$80x \ = \ 1600$$
$$x \ = \ 20\ m.$$

           Answer: Amount to be given exceeds capacity of tuber-
                         culin syringe so use hypodermic syringe and
                         administer 1.25 ml. or 20 m. of the U. 80
                         regular insulin by deep subcutaneous injection
                         immediately.

Tuberculin syringes have a 1-ml. volume. They have two scales; one is calibrated in minims, the other in hundredths of a ml. When small volumes of insulin are to be given one can more accurately determine the correct dosage by using a tuberculin syringe than by using a hypodermic syringe.

| Problem 2. | Ordered: | Regular insulin 4 units a.c. q. a.m. |
| | Available: | Regular insulin U. 40 and no insulin syringe. |

Solution:

$$U. 40 : 1 \text{ ml.} = U. 4 : x \text{ ml.}$$
$$40x = 4$$
$$x = 0.1 \text{ ml.}$$

| | Answer: | Use tuberculin syringe and give 0.1 ml. of U. 40 regular insulin before breakfast every morning. |

Sometimes two kinds of insulin are given at the same time, as in the following problem. When more than one concentration of insulin are available select the one which permits the administration of the most reasonable amount. In general, the amount should not exceed 1 ml. when possible.

Problem 3.	Ordered:	Regular insulin 16 units c̄ N.P.H.
		Insulin 30 units a.c. q. a.m.
	Available:	Regular insulin U. 40 and N.P.H. insulin U. 80, and no insulin syringes.

Solution:

$$U. 40 : 16 \text{ m.} = U. 16 : x \text{ m.}$$
$$40x = 256$$
$$x = 6.4 \text{ m. regular insulin, plus}$$

$$U. 80 : 16 \text{ m.} = U. 30 : x \text{ m.}$$
$$80x = 480$$
$$x = 6 \text{ m. N.P.H. insulin}$$

| | Answer: | Using a hypodermic or, preferably, a tuberculin syringe measure 6.4 m. of U. 40 regular insulin. Next, fill the syringe to the 12.4-m. mark when adding the U. 80 N.P.H. insulin. Administer before breakfast every morning. |

Problem 4.	Ordered:	Regular insulin 16 U. c̄ N.P.H. insulin 30 U. a.c. q. a.m.
	Available:	Regular insulin U. 40 and U. 80, N. P. H. insulin U. 80, and a 1-ml. U. 40 and U. 80 scale insulin syringe.
	Answer:	Using the U. 80 scale on the syringe fill to the 16-unit mark with U. 80 regular insulin. When adding U. 80 N.P.H. insulin fill to the 46-unit mark on the U. 80 scale of the syringe.

Problem 5.   *Ordered:*   Regular insulin 200 units stat. (rarely ordered).
              Available: Regular insulin U. 80 and all syringes shown
                            above (No U. 100 regular insulin readily
                            available).

Solution::   U. 80 : 1 ml. = U. 200 : x ml.
                                                     80x = 200
                                                       x = 2.5 ml.

              Answer: One could use a 2.5-ml. or a 5-ml. hypodermic
                            syringe to give 2.5 ml. of U. 80 regular insulin
                            stat, after verifying the order. One could also
                            fill the 3-ml. insulin syringe shown above to the
                            100-unit mark on the U. 40 scale.

Problem 6.   *Ordered:*   Lente insulin 18 U. q.d.
              Available: Lente insulin U. 80 and no insulin syringes.

Solution: U. 80 : 16 m. = U. 18 : x m.
                                                     80x = 288
                                                       x = 3.6 m.

              Answer: Using a tuberculin syringe administer 3.6 m.
                            U. 80 lente insulin every day.

Practice Problems:

1. *Ordered:*   Regular insulin iv units 20 min. a.c. t.i.d.
    Available: Iletin (regular) insulin U. 40 and no insulin syringes.

    Answer:...

2. *Ordered:*   P.Z.I. insulin 18 units 4 p.m. q.d.
    Available: Protamine zinc insulin (P.Z.I.) U. 40 and a U. 80 scale
    insulin syringe and hypodermic and tuberculin syringes.

    Answer:...

3. *Ordered:*   Regular insulin v̄ units 20 min. a.c. t.i.d.
    Available: Crystalline zinc (regular) insulin U. 40 and no insulin
    syringes.

    Answer:...

4. *Ordered:*   Zinc insulin 24 units 1 hr. a.c. breakfast q.d.
    Available: Globin zinc insulin U. 40 and U. 80 and a 1-ml. U. 40 and
    U. 80 scale insulin syringe.

    Answer:...

5. *Ordered:*   N.P.H. insulin 45 units and regular insulin 24 units 1 hr.
                   a.c. breakfast tomorrow.
    Available: Isophane insulin suspension (N.P.H.) U. 40 and U. 80 and
                   Iletin (regular) insulin U. 40 and U. 80 and a U. 40 and
                   U. 80 scale insulin syringe.

    Answer: ....

6. *Ordered:*   Lente insulin 46 units 1 hr. a.c. breakfast q.d.
    Available: Insulin zinc suspension (lente) U. 40 and a U. 80 scale
                   insulin syringe and hypodermic and tuberculin syringes.

    Answer: ....

7. *Ordered:*   Ultra-lente insulin U. 65 1 hr. a.c. breakfast tomorrow.
    Available: Insulin zinc suspension, extended (Ultra-Lente Iletin) U. 40
                   and U. 80 and a U. 80 scale insulin syringe.

    Answer: ....

8. *Ordered:*   Semi-lente insulin 18 U. 1/2 hr. a.c. breakfast q.d.
    Available: Insulin zinc suspension, prompt (Semi-Lente Iletin) U. 40
                   and U. 80 and no insulin syringes.

    Answer: ....

52

9. *Ordered:*   Ultra-lente insulin 46 units 1 hr. a.c. breakfast q.d.
   Available: Ultra-lente insulin U. 40 and U. 80 and U. 40 and U. 80 scale insulin syringes.

   Answer:..

10. *Ordered:*   Regular insulin 15 units and N.P.H. insulin 30 units 1/2 hr. a.c. breakfast q. a.m.
    Available: Crystalline zinc (regular) insulin U. 40 and isophane insulin suspension (N.P.H.) U. 40 and a U. 40 scale insulin syringe.

    Answer:..

11. *Ordered:*   Regular insulin U. 36 15 min. a.c. t.i.d.
    Available: Iletin, regular unmodified (regular) insulin U. 40 and no insulin syringes.

    Answer:..

12. *Ordered:*   Lente insulin 35 U. and regular insulin 10 U. 20 min. a.c. q. a.m.
    Available: Lente insulin U. 40 and U. 80 and regular insulin U. 40 and U. 80 and all kinds of syringes.

    Answer:..

INTRAVENOUS FLUIDS AND MEDICATIONS

When administering fluids intravenously it is often necessary for nurses to calculate and regulate the drops per minute in order to give a certain amount in the ordered period of time. The administration sets made by various manufacturers are constructed to yield varying numbers of drops per milliliter. This information may be found on the box containing the set. Examples are as follows:

10 drops/ml. - Mead and Baxter
15 drops/ml. - Abbott
20 drops/ml. - Cutter
60 drops/ml. - One example of size of pediatric administration set made by various companies.

Formulas A, B, and C cannot be used for calculating the regulation of intravenous fluids. Steps involved in calculating drops per minute include determining:

a. ml./hr $\dfrac{\text{total ml. fluid to be given}}{\text{hrs. to be run}}$ = desired ml./hr.

b. gtts./hr. desired ml./hr. x drops per ml. = gtts./hr.

c. gtts./min. $\dfrac{\text{desired gtts./hr.}}{60 \text{ min.}}$ = gtts./min.

Steps b and c can easily be reversed or they can also be combined as follows:

Baxter sets

$\dfrac{\text{ml./hr.}}{6}$ = gtts./min.

Abbott sets

$\dfrac{\text{ml./hr.}}{4}$ = gtts./min.

Cutter sets

$\dfrac{\text{ml./hr.}}{3}$ = gtts./min.

60 gtts./ml. microsets

ml./hr. = gtts./min.

Examples:

Problem 1.   *Ordered:*   Give 1000 ml. 5% dextrose in water (D-5-W) I.V. in 2 hrs.
   Available: Abbott administration set.

Solution:

$$1000 \text{ ml. } \div 2 = 500 \text{ ml./hr.}$$
$$500 \text{ ml. } x \text{ 15 gtts./ml.} = 7500 \text{ gtts./hr.}$$
$$7500 \text{ gtts. } \div 60 \text{ min.} = 125 \text{ gtts./min.}$$

or

$$1000 \div 2 = 500 \text{ ml./hr.}$$
$$500 \div 60 = 8\text{-}1/3 \text{ ml./min.}$$
$$8\text{-}1/3 \text{ x } 15 = 125 \text{ gtts./min.}$$

or

$$1000 \div 2 = 500 \text{ ml./hr.}$$
$$500 \div 4 = 125 \text{ gtts./min.}$$

Answer: Regulate I.V. to flow at 125 drops per minute initially.

Problem 2.   *Ordered:* Give 2000 ml. D-5-W q.d. by continuous drip.
              Available: Baxter administration set.

Solution:

$$2000 \div 24 = 83\text{-}1/3 \text{ ml./hr.}$$
$$83\text{-}1/3 \text{ x } 10 = 833 \text{ gtts./hr.}$$
$$833\text{-}1/3 \div 60 = 13.88\text{-}1/3 \text{ or } 14 \text{ gtts./min.}$$

or

$$2000 \div 24 = 83\text{-}1/3 \text{ ml./hr.}$$
$$83\text{-}1/3 \div 60 = 25/18 \text{ ml./min.}$$
$$25/18 \text{ x } 10 = 250/18 = 13\text{-}8/9 \text{ or } 14 \text{ gtts./min.}$$

or

$$2000 \div 24 = 83\text{-}1/3 \text{ ml./hr.}$$
$$83\text{-}1/3 \div 6 = 250/18 = 13.88\text{-}1/3 \text{ or } 14 \text{ gtts./min.}$$

Answer: Regulate to flow at 14 drops per minute initially.

Nurses should check the rate of flow of intravenous fluids at least every 15 minutes for infants and children and at least every 30 minutes for adults. It is not enough to count the drops per minute at these intervals because the fluid may have been running faster or slower than it should have been sometime during this interval. Therefore, every time one checks, refigure the rate of flow needed after determining how much fluid is left and in what period of time it is to be administered. See example below.

Problem 3.	Ordered:	Give 1000 ml. D-5-W in 2 hrs. (When started at 9 a.m., the I.V. was regulated to flow at 125 gtts./min. Upon checking the bottle at 9:30 a.m. one finds 450 ml. left in the bottle.)
	Available:	Abbott administration set.

Solution:

$$450 \text{ ml.} \div 1\text{-}1/2 \text{ hr.} = 300 \text{ ml./hr.}$$
$$300 \text{ ml./hr.} \div 60 \text{ min.} = 5 \text{ ml./min.}$$
$$5 \text{ ml.} \times 15 \text{ gtts.} = 75 \text{ gtts./min.}$$

Answer: At 9:30 a.m. regulate the flow of the fluid at 75 drops per minute, or less if indicated.

Problem 4.	Ordered:	Give 1000 ml. D-5-W c̄ 40 mEq. potassium chloride (KCl) I.V. today.
	Available:	Cutter administration set.

Solution:

40 mEq. ÷ 20 mEq. = 2 hrs.
(Considering that to prevent intoxication no more than 20 to 25 mEq. KCl per hour should be given intravenously to adults this solution with 40 mEq. should run about 2 hrs. Other factors, however, should be considered when regulating the rate of flow in order to prevent dehydration, cardiac or respiratory embarrassment, and so forth.)

$$1000 \text{ ml.} \div 2 \text{ hrs.} = 500 \text{ ml./hr.}$$
$$500 \text{ ml.} \times 20 \text{ gtts./ml.} = 10,000 \text{ gtts./hr.}$$
$$10,000 \text{ gtts.} \div 60 \text{ min.} = 166\text{-}2/3 \text{ or}$$
$$167 \text{ gtts./min.}$$

Answer: Regulate I.V. to flow at 167 drops per minute initially.

Problem 5.	*Ordered:*	2000 cc. D-5-W I.V. to run 24 hrs.
		(When started at 10 a.m. the I.V. was regulated to flow at 14 gtts./min. See Problem 2 above. Now it is 12 noon the same day and 400 ml. remains in the first 1000-ml. bottle.)
	Available:	Baxter administration set.

Solution:

$$400 \text{ ml.} \div 10 \text{ hrs.} = 40 \text{ ml./hr.}$$
$$40 \text{ ml.} \div 6 = 6\text{-}2/3 \text{ or}$$
$$7 \text{ gtts./min.}$$

Answer: Regulate the I.V. to flow at 7 drops per minute. (The first 1000 ml. was to run 12 hrs.; 10 of those 12 hrs. remain. Calculating on the basis of the 2000 ml. in 24 hrs. would result in greater fluid infusion in the first 12 hrs. than during the second 12 hrs.)

Problem 6.	*Ordered:*	(Infant weighing 11 lbs.) 200 ml. Ringer's lactate I.V. q.d.
	Available:	Microdrip (60 gtts./ml.) administration set.

Solution:

$$200 \text{ ml.} \div 24 \text{ hrs.} = 8\text{-}1/3 \text{ ml./hr.}$$
$$8\text{-}1/3 \text{ ml.} \times 60 \text{ gtts./ml.} = 500 \text{ gtts./ml.}$$
$$500 \text{ gtts.} \div 60 \text{ min.} = 8\text{-}1/3 \text{ gtts./min.}$$

(Note than when using 60 gtts./ml. microdrip sets the desired ml./hr. equals the desired gtts./min. because one divides the ml./hr. by 60 min./hr. then multiplies the ml./hr. by 60 gtts./ml.)

Answer: Regulate the I.V. to flow at 8 drops per min.

Calculated infusion flow rates are guidelines only. Maintaining the calculated rate of flow does not relieve nurses of their responsibility to observe for indications of too rapid or too slow infusion. Fulfilling one's obligation to speed up, slow down or stop an intravenous infusion at any time requires considerable nursing judgment based upon many factors which are far beyond the scope of this book.

Practice Problems:

1. *Ordered:*   1000 cc. D-5-W I.V. to run 4 hrs.
   Available: Abbott administration set.

   Answer: ....

2. *Ordered:*   1000 ml. D-5-W and 1000 ml. isotonic saline I.V. today.
   Available: Cutter administration set. (Considering all the factors indicated one decides that this solution should run at least 4 hrs.)

   Answer: ....

3. *Ordered:*   500 ml. D-5-W c̄ 40 mEq potassium chloride I.V. today.
   Available: Baxter administration set.

   Answer: ....

4. *Ordered:*   1000 ml. isotonic saline and 2000 ml. D-5-W I.V. to run 24 hrs.
   Available: Abbott administration set. (I.V. was started at 10 a.m.)

   Answer: ....

5. *Ordered:*   Same as in Problem 4 above.
   Available: Same as in Problem 4 above. (At noon the same day 700 ml. remain in the first bottle.)

   Answer:..

6. *Ordered:*   (25-lb. infant) Add 400 ml. 1/6 M Ringer's lactate to I.V. and run 24 hrs.
   Available: Microdrip (60 gtts./ml.) administration set.

   Answer:..

7. *Ordered:*   1000 ml. D-10-W I.V. to run from 9 a.m. to 3 p.m. today.
   Available: Baxter administration set.

   Answer:..

8. *Ordered:*   Same as in Problem 7 above.
   Available: Same as in Problem 7 above. (At 10 a.m. there are 800 ml. in the bottle.)

   Answer:..

9. *Ordered:*   Add 5,000,000 U. aqueous penicillin to q. 1000 ml. D-5-W I.V. and give 500,000 U. penicillin q.h.

   Available: Cutter administration set.

   Answer: ....

10. *Ordered:*   Same as in Problem 9 above.

   Available: Same as in Problem 9 above. (The I.V. was started at 4 p.m. and at 4:30 p.m. there are 950 ml. in the bottle.)

   Answer: ....

11. *Ordered:*   (10-lb. infant) Add 300 ml. D-5-W when present I.V. absorbed and give 10 ml./hr.

   Available: Microdrip (60 gtts./ml.) administration set.

   Answer: ....

12. *Ordered:*   (1-year-old baby) Add 500 ml. 1/2 N saline to I.V. stat and run 24 hrs.

   Available: Microdrip (60 gtts./ml.) administration set.

   Answer: ....

CHAPTER IV
PREPARING SOLUTIONS
FOR TOPICAL USE

In the preceding calculations of dosage problems the strength of available drugs was not changed. Therefore, a direct ratio and proportion was used to determine merely how much of the available drug should be given to administer the ordered dosage. When preparing solutions for topical use one is changing the percentage or ratio strength of the drugs to a weaker strength, or to the strength ordered to be used. This requires the use of an indirect ratio and proportion such as Formula C, given earlier. Formula C can be used to solve all types of solution problems, which include:

1. Preparing solutions from tablets, powders, or crystals (always 100% strength)
2. Preparing solutions from stock solutions
   a. from 100% or full-strength solutions
   b. from less than full-strength solutions

Formula C may be interpreted as follows:

known strengths of solutions	amount of stronger drug or solution	amount of weaker solution
5% : 100%	= x ml. (or Gm.)	: 1000 ml.

This formula may also be interpreted as follows:

small % strength : large % strength = small volume : large volume

or as

weaker : stronger = solute : solvent

In all solutions problems the first term of the proportion will be determined by the doctor's order for a solution of particular strength. The second term will be determined by the strength of stock drug or solution which is available for one's use in the clinical nursing area. The third term will almost always be the unknown amount of solute to be used; for example, how many grain 1 tablets or how much 100% solution should be used to make a certain amount of the ordered strength solution? The fourth term, or the total amount of solution to be prepared, will usually be determined by the nurse on the basis of need. One will determine, for example, that one gallon of potassium permanganate solution will be needed for a foot soak. Possible exceptions to the above will be discussed later. The solvent will usually be water, either tap water or sterile distilled water. This may be summarized as:

1st term	:	2nd term	=	3rd term	:	4th term
strength Dr. orders	:	strength of stock drug	=	? stock drug needed	:	amount nurse needs

Though one is changing the strength of the solution or drug, one is not changing the amount of drug; therefore, the product of the means will always equal the product of the extremes and both of these values equal the amount of drug used. One can check the accuracy of stating the ratio and proportion by determining the following:

1. Multiplication of the means should involve multiplying the amount of the greater strength stock drug or solution by the strength of this drug or solution.

2. Multiplication of the extremes should involve multiplying the amount of the weaker strength prepared solution by the strength of this solution.

TABLETS, POWDERS, OR CRYSTALS

Though the drugs added to the solvent will often increase the total volume slightly, the amount of increase is too small to make any appreciable difference when preparing large amounts of solution. Also, the displacement by the drug may be 0.5 ml. or 2 ml., for example, and one may be using a 1-liter pitcher, with a mark for every 50 ml., to measure the solvent. It is impossible to measure accurately enough to account for these small displacement amounts. Therefore, the amount of displacement by the drug is not considered when the drug is in tablet, crystal, or powder form.

Because in actual practice the containers available for measurement of large volumes will be calibrated for every 50 or 100 ml., for example, accurate measurement of the stock drug or solution to within a fraction of a milliliter or even to within a few milliliters will not be possible. It may be necessary to measure small amounts of solute in a 1-ounce container, for example, and to measure the solvent in another container.

Examples

Problem 1. *Ordered:* Warm saturated boric acid solution soaks of left foot 20 min. stat. (Assume one needs 1 gal. of this solution.)

        Available: Boric acid crystals.

Solution: A 5% boric acid solution is a saturated one.

weaker strength	stronger strength	smaller amount of stronger drug	larger amount of weaker solution
5%	: 100%	= x Gm. (ml).	: 4000 ml.
	100 x	= 20,000	
	x	= 200 Gm. (ml.)	

        Answer: Add 200 ml. boric acid crystals to 1 gal. warm water.

Weighing 200 Gm. of boric acid crystals would be more accurate than measuring 200 ml. of the drug, but scales are not available in clinical areas or in homes. When preparing solutions for topical use, attaining the exact ordered strength is not as important as when giving oral or parenteral dosages. Therefore, one may safely substitute ml. for Gm. when measuring powders or crystals.

Problem 2. *Ordered:* N.S. enema p.r.n. (One decides to prepare 2 qts. of this solution.)

        Available: Table salt.

Solution:

weaker	stronger	solute	solvent
0.9%	: 100%	= x Gm. (ml.)	: 2000 ml.
	100x	= 1800.0	
	x	= 18 Gm. (ml).	

        Answer: Add 18 ml. table salt to 2 qts. of tap water at the appropriate temperature. (Because of the heavy molecular weight of sodium chloride one may use 2 tsp. salt per qt. of water when preparing isotonic saline solutions.)

(Here, and several times previously, the abbreviation "N.S." has been used for normal saline. Normal saline is a 5.8% strength solution, but the term N.S. is frequently used as a substitute for the term isotonic saline which is a 0.9% strength solution. Normal saline solutions are rarely used for any purpose because they are physiologically hypertonic rather than isotonic. Unless otherwise indicated "N.S." should be considered to be a 0.9% strength solution.)

If the first term is stated as a fraction then the second term must also be stated as a fraction. The third term must be a weight unit of measure which equals the volume unit of measure of the fourth term. See sample below.

Problem 3.   *Ordered:*   1:8000 potassium permanganate ($KMNO_4$) compresses to right lower leg 20 min. q.i.d. (Assume one needs 1 qt. of this solution.)

Available: $KMNO_4$ tablets 1 gr. and 5 gr.

Solution:

small or weaker	large or stronger	small volume	large volume

$$1/8000 \; : \; 1/1 \quad = \; x \text{ Gm.} : 1000 \text{ ml.}$$
$$1x \quad = \frac{1000}{8000} = 1/8$$
$$x \quad = 1/8 \text{ Gm.} = 2 \text{ gr.}$$

Answer: Dissolve 2 of the 1-gr. tablets of $KMNO_4$ in 1000 ml. sterile water. (The nurse chooses sterile water as the solvent because the patient has an open lesion on his leg.)

(A potassium permanganate solution may be used for bactericidal or bacteriostatic action because it is an oxidizing agent. Exposure to light or heat before use causes loss of oxygen which makes the solution ineffective as an antiseptic or germicidal solution. Therefore, prepared solutions should not be heated and they should be stored in a dark, cool place. Also, potassium permanganate stains fabrics and skin. The stains are difficult to remove.)

Problem 4.   *Ordered:*   1:12,000 potassium permanganate ($KMNO_4$) soaks of left hand 20 min. q.i.d. (One needs 1000 ml. solution per treatment.)

Available: $KMNO_4$ tablets 1 gr. and 5 gr.

Solution:

$$1/12,000 : 1/1 \quad = \; x \text{ Gm.} : 1000 \text{ ml.}$$
$$1x \quad = \frac{1000}{12,000} = 1/12$$
$$x \quad = 1/12 \text{ Gm.}$$

$$15 \text{ gr.} : 1 \text{ Gm.} = x \text{ gr.} : 1/12 \text{ Gm.}$$
$$1x = 15/12 = 1\text{-}1/4$$
$$x = 1\text{-}1/4 \text{ gr.}$$

or

$$16 \text{ gr.} : 1 \text{ Gm.} = x \text{ gr.} : 1/12 \text{ Gm.}$$
$$1x = 16/12 = 1\text{-}1/3$$
$$x = 1\text{-}1/3 \text{ gr.}$$

One cannot accurately prepare this amount of 1:12,000 $KMNO_4$ with the available tablets which cannot be divided. One can prepare more than 1000 ml., using 2 gr. (1/8 Gm.) $KMNO_4$, as shown below.

$$1/12,000 : 1/1 = 1/8 \text{ Gm.} : x \text{ ml.}$$
$$1/12,000x = 1/8$$
$$x = 1/8 \times \frac{12,000}{1} = \frac{12,000}{8}$$
$$x = 1500 \text{ ml.}$$

Answer: Dissolve 2 of the 1-gr. $KMNO_4$ tablets in 1500 ml. water.

One could also prepare a stock solution, for example, a 1:1000 (1 Gm. : 1000 ml.) solution, by adding 3 of the 5-gr. tablets to 1000 ml. water. This stock solution could then be diluted to the ordered strength, as will be shown later. Because $KMNO_4$ tablets dissolve so slowly this method may be preferred when treatments are to be done frequently.

Occasionally one must use Formula C for preparing solutions for oral rather than topical use.

Problem 5.   *Ordered:*   250 ml. 1/2 isotonic saline p.o. q.h. x 4.

Available: Table salt and home cooking measures.

Solution: $0.45\% : 100\% = x \text{ Gm. (ml.)} : 1000 \text{ ml.}$
$$100x = 450$$
$$x = 4.5 \text{ Gm. or ml.}$$

Answer: Add 1 tsp. salt to a qt. of water if preparing entire amount at one time or 1/4 tsp. salt to a glass of water if preparing 250 ml. at a time.

Problem 6.   *Ordered:*   Sterile warm 2% boric acid compresses continuously today. (One wants to dissolve all of the drug.)

               Available: One oz. of boric acid crystals.

Solution:

$$2\% : 100\% = 30 \text{ Gm.(ml.)} : x \text{ ml.}$$
$$2x = 3000$$
$$x = 1500 \text{ ml.}$$

               Answer: Dissolve the 1 oz. of boric acid crystals in 1-1/2 qts. sterile water.

Practice Problems

1. *Ordered:*   N.S. enema stat. (Assume that one needs 1 qt. of this solution.)
   Available: Sodium chloride crystals.

   Answer: ....

2. *Ordered:*   Irrigate both eyes with 3% sodium bicarbonate solution stat.
   (One wants to prepare 2 qts. solution.)
   Available: Sodium bicarbonate.

   Answer: ....

3. *Ordered:*   1000 ml. mercuric chloride 1:1000 for disinfection purpose.
   Available: Mercury bichloride tablets 0.5 Gm. and 0.12 Gm.

   Answer: ....

4. *Ordered:*   Paint feet c̄ 1% gentian violet b.i.d. q.d. (Prepare 1 oz.)
   Available: Gentian violet tablets 10 mg., 15 mg. and 30 mg.

   Answer: ....

5. *Ordered:* 1:10,000 potassium permanganate (KMNO$_4$) soaks of both legs 20 min. t.i.d. (One needs 1 gal. solution.)
   Available: KMNO$_4$ tablets 1 gr. and 5 gr.

   Answer: ....

6. *Ordered:* 1:8000 potassium permanganate (KMNO$_4$) bladder irrigation q.d. (Add tablets to 1000 ml. sterile water.)
   Available: KMNO$_4$ tablets 1 gr. and 5 gr.

   Answer: ....

7. *Ordered:* 1:15,000 potassium permanganate (KMNO$_4$) bladder irrigation q.d.
   Available: KMNO$_4$ tablets 5 gr. and 1000-ml. bottles of sterile water.

   Answer: ....

8. *Ordered:* 250 ml. 5% dextrose p.o. t.i.d.
   Available: Dextrose powder.

   Answer: ....

STOCK SOLUTIONS

When doing problems involving the dilution of solutions to make weaker strength solutions the fourth term of the proportion will be the total amount of weaker strength solution desired. The amount of solvent to be used in such instances will be the difference between the fourth and third terms or the total amount to be made minus the amount of solute.

Examples:

Problem 1. *Ordered:* Potassium permanganate ($KMNO_4$) 1:12,000 compresses to left hand 20 min. q.i.d. (Assume one needs 1000 ml. of this solution.)

Available: $KMNO_4$ 1:8000

Solution:

$$\frac{\text{weaker}}{\text{strength}} : \frac{\text{stronger}}{\text{strength}} = \frac{\text{smaller amount or solute}}{} : \frac{\text{larger amount or solvent}}{}$$

$$\frac{1}{12,000} : \frac{1}{8000} = \text{x ml.} : 1000 \text{ ml}$$

$$\frac{1}{8000x} = \frac{1000}{12,000}$$

$$1x = 1/12 \text{ x } \frac{8000}{1} = \frac{8000}{12}$$

$$x = 666\text{-}2/3 \text{ ml.}$$

Answer: Add 333-1/3 ml. water to 666-2/3 ml. $KMNO_4$ 1:8000. (These amounts cannot be measured this accurately, of course.)

Problem 2. *Ordered:* Potassium permanganate ($KMNO_4$) 1:10,000 bladder irrigation q.d. (One decides to prepare 1000 ml. solution.)

Available: $KMNO_4$ 1:1000

Solution:

$$\frac{\text{weaker}}{} \quad \frac{\text{stronger}}{} \quad \frac{\text{solute}}{} \quad \frac{\text{solvent}}{}$$

$$\frac{1}{10,000} : \frac{1}{1000} = \text{x ml.} : 1000 \text{ ml.}$$

$$\frac{1}{1000x} = \frac{1000}{10,000}$$

$$1x = \frac{1}{10} \text{ x } \frac{1000}{1} = \frac{1000}{10}$$

$$x = 100 \text{ ml.}$$

Answer: Add 100 ml. $KMNO_4$ 1:1000 to 900 ml. sterile water.

Problem 3.	*Ordered:*	30% alcohol cooling sponge stat. (Assume one needs 2 qts. solution.)		
	Available:	70% isopropyl alcohol.		

<table>
<tr><td rowspan="2">Solution:</td><td>small or
weaker</td><td>large or
stronger</td><td>small
volume</td><td>large
volume</td></tr>
</table>

$$30\% \quad : \quad 70\% \; = \; x \text{ ml. : } 2000 \text{ ml.}$$
$$70x \; = \; 60{,}000$$
$$x \; = \; 857\text{-}1/7 \text{ ml.}$$

Answer: Use 857-1/7 ml. 70% alcohol and 1142-6/7 ml. tap. water.

Problem 4.   *Ordered:*   30% alcohol cooling sponge stat.

Available: 1 pt. of 70% isopropyl rubbing alcohol. (One wants to dilute the entire bottle.)

Solution:

$$30\% : 70\% \; = \; 500 \text{ ml. : } x \text{ ml.}$$
$$30x \; = \; 35{,}000$$
$$x \; = \; 1166\text{-}1/3 \text{ ml. } (30\%)$$
$$\underline{-500 \text{ ml. } (70\%)}$$
$$666\text{-}2/3 \text{ ml. } (H_2O)$$

Answer: Add 666–2/3 ml. tap water to the pt. of 70% alcohol.

Problem 5.   *Ordered:*   2% Lysol solution for disinfecting excreta. (One needs 3 qts. solution.)

Available: Saponated cresol (Lysol) solution 1:2.

Solution:

$$2\% \; : \; 50\% = x \text{ ml. : } 3000 \text{ ml.}$$
$$50x \; = \; 6000$$
$$x \; = \; 120 \text{ ml.}$$

or

$$2/100 : 1/2 \; = \; x \text{ ml. : } 3000 \text{ ml.}$$
$$1/2x \; = \; \frac{2}{100} x \frac{3000}{1} = \frac{6000}{100}$$
$$1x \; = \; \frac{60}{1} x \frac{2}{1} = \frac{120}{1}$$
$$x \; = \; 120 \text{ ml.}$$

Answer: Add 2880 ml. water to 120 ml. 1:2 Lysol.

Problem 6.   *Ordered:*   Dilute hydrogen peroxide 1:4 and use as mouthwash p.r.n. (One needs 1 oz. for each treatment.)

 Available: Hydrogen peroxide (3%)

Solution:

$$1/4 \; : \; 1/1 \; = \; x \text{ ml.} \; : \; 32 \text{ ml.}$$
$$1x \; = \; \frac{32}{4} \; = \; 8$$
$$x \; = \; 8 \text{ ml.}$$

or

$$1 \; : \; 4 \; = \; x \text{ ml.} \; : \; 32 \text{ ml.}$$
$$4x \; = \; 32$$
$$x \; = \; 8 \text{ ml.}$$

 Answer: Use 8 ml. of 3% hydrogen peroxide and 24 ml. water. (There are 20% hydrogen peroxide preparations but these are not for medicinal use.)

Practice Problems

1. *Ordered:* Keep suction catheter in Zephiran Chloride 1:5000. (One needs 1 pt. solution each time solution is changed.)

   Available: Benzalkonium chloride (Zephiran Cl) 1:1000.

   Answer: ....

2. *Ordered:* 4 oz. 2.5% dextrose solution p.o. q.3h.

   Available: 50-ml. ampules 50% dextrose and 500-ml. and 1000-ml. bottles of 5% and 10% dextrose.

   Answer: ....

3. *Ordered:* Irrigate bladder c̄ 60 cc. potassium permanganate (KMNO₄) 1 : 12,000 b.i.d. (One decides to prepare 1 qt. of this solution.)

   Available: 1 gal. of KMNO₄ 1:10,000.

   Answer: ....

4. *Ordered:* Use isolation technique. (One needs 1 gal. 70% alcohol for disinfecting equipment.)

   Available: Ethyl alcohol 95% in 1-gal. bottles.

   Answer: ....

5. *Ordered:* Apply 1:1000 Adrenalin to left nostril stat.
   Available: Epinephrine solution 1:100 (non-sterile).

   Answer: ....

6. *Ordered:* Hydrogen peroxide 1:3 as mouthwash q.i.d. (One needs 1 oz. each time.)
   Available: Hydrogen peroxide (3%) in 1-pt. bottles.

   Answer: ....

7. *Ordered:* Soak both feet in Dakin's solution (0.5%) 15 min. t.i.d. (One needs 2 qts. for each treatment.)
   Available: Sodium hypochlorite solution 5%.

   Answer: ....

8. *Ordered:* Irrigate left eye c̄ 2% boric acid solution q.i.d. (Assume one wants to prepare 500 ml. sterile solution.)
   Available: Sterile 5% boric acid solution.

   Answer: ....

CHAPTER V

REVIEW PROBLEMS

1. *Ordered:* Quinidine 3 gr. I.M. stat.
   Available: 10 cc. vial of quinidine gluconate injection 80 mg. per ml.

   Answer: ....

2. *Ordered:* 2000 ml. D-5-W I.V. in 24 hrs.
   Available: Abbott administration set.

   Answer: ....

3. *Ordered:* Lente insulin 50 units 1 hr. a.c. breakfast tomorrow.
   Available: Insulin zinc suspension (lente) U.40 and a U.80 scale insulin syringe and hypodermic syringes.

   Answer: ....

4. *Ordered:* ASA 0.6 Gm. q. 3 to 4 h. p.r.n. for pain or fever over 102°F.
   Available: Acetylsalicylic acid (ASA) 5-gr. tablets.

   Answer: ....

5. *Ordered:* Bejectal 1 ml. I.M. twice weekly.
   Available: Combination package of 2 vials to make 10.6 ml. of Bejectal solution.

   Answer: ....

6. *Ordered:* Potassium permanganate (KMNO$_4$) 1:12,000 compresses to left hand 20 min. q.i.d. prior to application of Terra-Cortril ointment. (Prepare 1 gal.)
   Available: KMNO$_4$ 1:8000 and 1-gr. and 5-gr. tablets.

   Answer: ....

7. *Ordered:* Nembutal 100 mg., atropine 0.4 mg., and Demerol 75 mg. "H" on call to surgery.
   Available: 2-ml. ampules of pentobarbital sodium (Nembutal) 1-1/2 gr. in 2 ml., atropine hypodermic tablets 1/150 gr., and 2-ml. ampules of meperidine hydrochloride (Demerol) 50 mg. per ml.

   Answer: ....

8. *Ordered:* (Infant) Kantrex 150 mg. I.M. q. 12 h.
   Available: Kanamycin sulfate (Kantrex) solution 0.5 Gm. per 2 cc.

   Answer: ....

9. *Ordered:*   Kaon Elixir 15 mEq. t.i.d.
    Available: A 4-oz. bottle of potassium gluconate (Kaon) 40 mEq. per oz.

    Answer: ....

10. *Ordered:*   Isotonic sodium chloride (NaCl) enema stat and p.r.n. (Prepare
                  2 qts.)
    Available: Sodium chloride crystals.

    Answer: ....

11. *Ordered:*   Aqueous buffered penicillin G 400,000 U. I.M. q.4 h.
    Available: A 20-ml. vial of buffered potassium penicillin G 1,000,000 U.
                  To get 250,000 U. per ml. add 3.6 ml. diluent.

    Answer: ....

12. *Ordered:*   Phenobarbital 1/2 gr. p.o. q.i.d.
    Available: Phenobarbital sodium tablets 30 mg. and 60 mg.

    Answer: ....

CHAPTER VI

CHILDREN'S DOSAGES

Only physicians prescribe dosages of medications, but nurses must know if ordered dosages are within the safe range for the individual patient before they carry out an order. This is especially true for infants and children. Since some textbooks do not include dosages of drugs for infants and children, many nurses may need to determine these from the known, usual adult dosages.

The rules below are the more commonly used procedures for determining dosages for infants and children from proper adult dosages. However, these rules should serve only as a guide to determining approximate child dosages. For example, using Young's or Fried's Rule to determine the correct dose for a child gives no consideration to the child's weight or size, an important factor. The physiologic and pathologic conditions must also be considered, as must the nature of the drug. Children have relatively less tolerance than adults do for narcotics, for instance. If after consideration of these factors nurses have any question about the dosage ordered, they should consult the physician.

YOUNG'S RULE (For children from 1 or 2 to 12 years)

$$\frac{\text{Age in years}}{\text{Age plus 12}} \quad x \quad \text{Adult dose} = \text{Child's dose}$$

FRIED'S RULE (For infants and children up to 1 or 2 years)

$$\frac{\text{Age in months}}{150} \quad x \quad \text{Adult dose} = \text{Infant's or child's dose}$$

CLARK'S RULE (For infants or children)

$$\frac{\text{Weight in pounds}}{150} \quad x \quad \text{Adult dose} = \text{Infant's or child's dose}$$

Examples:

Problem 1.   *Ordered:*   (8-year-old child) Gantrisin suspension 0.4 Gm. q.4h.

           Adult dose: 1 Gm. every 4 hrs.

Solution: Young's Rule

$$\frac{8}{8 + 12} \times 1 \text{ Gm.} = \frac{8}{20} = 2/5 \text{ or } 0.4 \text{ Gm.}$$

Answer: The ordered dose is reasonable.

Problem 2.   *Ordered:*   (4-month-old baby) PAS solution 50 mg.
                                   q.i.d.
               Adult dose: 2 to 4 Gm. q.i.d.

Solution: Fried's Rule

$$\frac{4}{150} \times 4 \text{ Gm.} = 16/150 \text{ Gm.} = 0.10\text{-}2/3 \text{ Gm. or}$$
                                   106.7 mg. (maximum
                                   dosage)

                            or

$$\frac{4}{150} \times 2 \text{ Gm.} = 8/150 \text{ Gm.} = 0.05\text{-}1/3 \text{ Gm. or } 53.3$$
                                   mg. (minimum dosage)

Answer: The ordered dose is just below the minimum
                 calculated recommended dosage.

Problem 3.   *Ordered:*   (4-month-old baby weighing 10 pounds)
                                   PAS solution 50 mg. q.i.d.

               Adult dose: 2 to 4 Gm. q.i.d.

Solution: Clark's Rule

$$\frac{10}{150} \times 2 \text{ Gm.} = 2/15 \text{ Gm.} = 0.1333 \text{ Gm. or } 133.3 \text{ mg.}$$
                                   (minimum dosage)

                            or

$$\frac{10}{150} \times 4 \text{ Gm.} = 4/15 \text{ Gm.} = 0.2667 \text{ Gm. or } 266.7 \text{ mg.}$$
                                   (maximum dosage)

Answer: The ordered dose is well below the calculated
                 minimum dosage.

Problem 4.   *Ordered:*   (4-month-old baby weighing 15 pounds)
                                   PAS solution 50 mg. q.i.d.

Adult dose: 2 to 4 Gm. q.i.d.

Solution: Clark's Rule

$$\frac{15}{150} \times 2 \text{ Gm.} = 2/10 \text{ Gm.} = 0.2 \text{ Gm. or 200 mg.}$$
(minimum dosage)

or

$$\frac{15}{150} \times 4 \text{ Gm.} = 4/10 \text{ Gm.} = 0.4 \text{ Gm. or 400 mg.}$$
(maximum dosage)

Answer: The ordered dosage is one-fourth the minimum recommended dosage as calculated.

These examples should illustrate that the use of different rules will yield different answers and that weight is one of several variables to be considered.

Problem 5.   *Ordered:*   (6-year-old child) M.S. 4 mg. q. 4h. p.r.n. for pain.

Adult dose: Usual is 15 mg.; range is 8 to 20 mg.

Solution: Young's Rule

$$\frac{6}{6 + 12} \times 8 \text{ mg.} = 6/18 \times 8 \text{ mg.} = 8/3 \text{ mg.} = 2.67 \text{ mg.}$$
(minimum dosage)

or

$$\frac{6}{6 + 12} \times 15 \text{ mg.} = 1/3 \times 15 \text{ mg.} = 5 \text{ mg. (usual dosage)}$$

or

$$\frac{6}{6 + 12} \times 20 \text{ mg.} = 1/3 \times 20 \text{ mg.} = 6.67 \text{ mg. (maximum dosage)}$$

Answer: The ordered dosage is within the recommended range.

Problem 6.   *Ordered:*   (A 6-year-old child weighing 50 pounds) M.S. 4 mg. q. 4h. p.r.n. for pain.

Adult dose: Usual is 15 mg.; range is 8 to 20 mg.

Solution: Clark's Rule

$$\frac{50}{150} \times 15 \text{ mg.} = 1/3 \times 15 \text{ mg.} = 5 \text{ mg. (usual dosage)}$$

Answer: The ordered dosage is reasonable.

In these two problems, the use of different rules has yielded the same answers.

Practice Problems:

1. *Ordered:*   (10-year-old male) Cortisone 12.5 mg. p.o. q.i.d.
   Adult dose: As much as 300 mg. first day down to daily maximum of 25 to 30 mg. for women and 40 to 45 mg. for men. Use Young's Rule.

   Answer: ....

2. *Ordered:*   (20-month-old child) Ephedrine liquid 3 mg. q.4h. p.r.n.
   Adult dose: Usual dose 25 mg. Use Fried's Rule.

   Answer: ....

3. *Ordered*   (3-year-old patient) Tincture digitoxin 0.02 mg. q.d.
   Adult dose: Usual maintenance dose is 0.1 mg. Use Young's Rule.

   Answer: ....

4. *Ordered:*   (1-year-old baby weighing 25 pounds) Cedilanid 0.025 mg. I.M. q.d.
   Adult dose: Usual maintenance dose is 1.0 mg. Use Clark's Rule.

   Answer: ....

5. *Ordered:*   (1-year-old baby weighing 25 pounds) Cedilanid 0.025 mg. I.M. q.d.

   Adult dose: Usual maintenance dose is 1.0 mg. Use Fried's Rule.

   Answer:..

6. *Ordered:*   (1-month-old infant weighing 7-1/2 pounds) Keflin 100 mg. I.M. q.6h.

   Adult dose: Usual dose is 0.5 to 1.0 Gm. I.M. q. 4 to 6 h. Use Clark's Rule.

   Answer: ....

7. *Ordered:*   (8-year-old child) Demerol 30 mg. "H" stat.

   Adult dose: Usual dose 50 to 100 mg. Use Young's Rule.

   Answer: ....

8. *Ordered:*   (1-year-old baby weighing 20 pounds) Atropine 0.1 mg. "H" stat.

   Adult dose: Usual dose is 0.5 mg. Use Clark's Rule.

   Answer: ....

APPENDIX A
SYSTEMS OF MEASUREMENT

HOUSEHOLD MEASURES

Nurses may use or teach the use of household articles for the measurement of drugs or solutions of drugs. Since household measures are not accurate, one should not substitute household equivalents for metric or apothecaries' measurements ordered by the physician. Note that all household measures are volume measurements. Occasionally, however, a volume measure will need to be used as a substitute for a weight measure. The equivalents below are approximate, not accurate.

TABLE 2. APPROXIMATE HOUSEHOLD EQUIVALENTS

Household	Household
60 drops (gtt.)	1 teaspoonful (tsp.)
2 teaspoonfuls	1 dessertspoonful
2 dessertspoonfuls (4 tsp.)	1 tablespoonful (tbsp.)
2 tablespoonfuls	1 fluid ounce
6 fluid ounces	1 teacupful
8 fluid ounces	1 glassful or 1 measuring cupful

Household	Apothecaries'	Metric
1 drop	1 minim	0.06 ml.
1 teaspoonful	1 fluid dram	4 or 5 ml.
1 tablespoonful	4 fluid drams	15 or 16 ml.
2 tablespoonfuls	1 fluid ounce	30 or 32 ml.
1 teacupful	6 fluid ounces	180 or 192 ml.
1 glassful or 1 measuring cupful	8 fluid ounces or 1/2 pint	240 or 250 ml.
2 glassfuls or 2 measuring cupfuls	16 fluid ounces or 1 pint	480 or 500 ml.
4 glassfuls or 4 measuring cupfuls	1 quart	960 or 1000 ml.

APOTHECARIES' SYSTEM

The apothecaries' system is one of several different and confusing old English systems of weights and measurement. The basic unit of weight in the apothecaries' system is the grain, originally the weight of a grain of wheat. The basic unit of fluid measure in this system is the minim, the approximate amount of water that would weigh one grain. Other units of measure which may be used in drug administration are given in Table 3. Additional apothecaries' units of measure rarely or never used by nurses in the administration of drugs are not included.

TABLE 3. APOTHECARIES' EQUIVALENTS

Weight Units	
60 grains (gr.)	1 dram (℥ or dr.)
8 drams (℥) or 480 grains	1 ounce (℥)
12 ounces (℥)	1 pound (lb.)

Fluid Units	
60 minims (m.)	1 fluid dram (fl. ℥)
8 fluid drams (fl. ℥) or 480 minims (m.)	1 fluid ounce (fl. ℥)
16 fluid ounces (fl. ℥)	1 pint (pt. or O.)
2 pints (pt. or O.)	1 quart (qt.)
4 quarts (qt.)	1 gallon (C or gal.)

*Weight Units	*Fluid Units
1 grain (gr.)	1 minim (m.)
60 grains (gr.)	1 fluid dram (fl. ℥), 60 m.
480 grains (gr.)	1 fluid ounce (fl. ℥), 480 m.

*The above apothecaries' weight-fluid units are approximate equivalents only but, when needed, these approximations are acceptable for the preparation and administration of solutions and drugs.

TABLE 4. APPROXIMATE APOTHECARIES'–METRIC VOLUME EQUIVALENTS

Apothecaries'	Metric
1 minim (m.)	0.06 milliliter (ml.)
4 m.	0.25 ml.
8 m.	0.5 ml.
15 or 16 m.	1 ml. or 1 cubic centimeter (cc.)
1 fluid dram or 60 or 64 m.	4 ml.
1 fluid ounce (fl. oz.) or 8 fl. drams	30 or 32 ml.
1 pint (pt.) or 16 fl. oz.	480 or 500 ml.
1 quart (qt.) or 32 fl. oz.	960 or 1000 ml. or 1 liter (L.)
1 gallon (gal.) or 128 fl. oz.	3840 or 4000 ml. or 4 L.

TABLE 5. COMMONLY USED APPROXIMATE APOTHECARIES'– METRIC WEIGHT EQUIVALENTS

Apothecaries'	Metric
1/60, 1/64, or 1/65 grain (gr.)	1 milligram (mg.) or 1000 micrograms (mcg.)
1 gr.	0.06, 0.064, or 0.065 gram (Gm.)
1 gr.	60, 64, or 65 mg.
1 gr.	60,000, 64,000, or 65,000 mcg.
5 gr.	0.3 or 0.33 Gm.
10 gr.	0.6 or 0.67 Gm.
15 or 16 gr.	1 Gm.
1 dram	4 Gm.
1 ounce	30 or 32 Gm.
1 pound (avoirdupois)	450 Gm.
2.2 pounds (imperial or avoirdupois—not apothecaries')	1 kilogram (kg.)
2.6 pounds (apothecaries'—which is not used by nurses)	1 kg.

METRIC SYSTEM

During the latter part of the eighteenth century the French devised the metric system based upon the decimal system and unalterable standards of measurement. Then in 1875 the International Bureau of Weights and Measures was established in Paris by the International Metric Convention. This Bureau prepared international standards for the participating countries.

The metric units of measurement are the *gram* (weight), *liter* (volume), and *meter* (linear). These basic units can be divided by or multiplied by 10, 100, or

1000. Latin prefixes are used to designate the subdivisions of these units and Greek prefixes are used to designate multiples of these units as shown below for the gram (Gm.)

1 kilogram (kg.)	=	1000. Gm.
1 hectogram (Hg.)	=	100. Gm.
1 dekagram (Dg.)	=	10. Gm.
1 gram (Gm.)	=	1.0 Gm.
1 decigram (dg.)	=	0.1 Gm.
1 centigram (cg.)	=	0.01 Gm.
1 milligram (mg.)	=	0.001 Gm.

The metric system of measurement has become the system of use in most of the world. Its use, especially in drug administration, is becoming more prevalent in the United States.

Gram

The gram, the metric unit of weight used in the pharmaceutical weighing of drugs, is equal to the weight of one milliliter of distilled water at 4°C. The kilogram (1000 Gm.) is the only multiple of the gram used by nurses. It may be used to calculate dosages, fluids, etc. in terms of kilograms of body weight. The only subdivisions of a gram commonly used are the milligram (0.001 Gm.) and the microgram (0.001 mg.).

Liter

The liter, the metric volume unit which is very frequently used by nurses, is equal to the contents of a one-decimeter (10 centimeters) cube. The liter was found to be 1000.028 cubic centimeters (cc.) rather than the 1000 cc. intended. A liter does contain 1000 milliliters (ml.), of course. Even though a cubic centimeter is 0.000028 cc. less than a milliliter, in drug administration a cubic centimeter and a milliliter are considered to be equal and are used interchangeably.

Since a gram is equal to the weight of one milliliter of distilled water at 4°C, *1 Gm. = 1 ml.* is an equivalent which may safely be used in the calculation of dosage and solutions problems when needed. This equivalent is an approximate not an accurate one when used for such purposes.

Meter

The meter, the metric linear unit of measurement, is 39.37 inches. Centimeters and millimeters, and occasionally microns (one thousandth of a millimeter), are the only linear metric measures used by nurses. There are approximately 2.5 centimeters per one inch. The sides of a cubic centimeter (cc.) are approximately 0.4 inch each.

TABLE 6. ADDITIONAL APPROXIMATE METRIC–APOTHECARIES' WEIGHT EQUIVALENTS

Metric		*Apothecaries'
	30 or 32 Gm.	1 oz.
	15 or 16 Gm.	4 dr.
	7.5 or 8 Gm.	2 dr.
	6 Gm.	90 to 96 gr.
	5 Gm.	75 to 80 gr.
	4 Gm.	60 to 64 gr. or 1 dr.
	3 Gm.	45 to 48 gr.
	2 Gm.	30 to 32 gr. or 1/2 dr.
	1.5 Gm.	22-1/2 to 24 gr.
1000 mg.	1 Gm.	15 to 16 gr.
750 mg.	0.75 Gm.	11-1/4 to 12 gr.
600 mg.	0.6 Gm.	9 to 9-3/5 gr. or 10 gr.
500 mg.	0.5 Gm	7-1/2 to 8 gr.
400 mg.	0.4 Gm.	6 to 6-2/5 gr.
300 mg.	0.3 Gm.	4-1/2 to 4-4/5 gr. or 5 gr.
250 mg.	0.25 Gm.	3-3/4 to 4 gr.
200 mg.	0.2 Gm.	3 to 3-1/5 gr.
150 mg.	0.15 Gm.	2-1/4 to 2-2/5 gr. or 2-1/2 gr.
120 mg.	0.12 Gm.	1-4/5 to 1-9/10 gr. or 2 gr.
100 mg.	0.1 Gm.	1-1/2 to 1-3/5 gr.
75 mg.	0.075 Gm.	1-1/8 to 101/5 gr.
60,64, or 65 mg.	0.06 to 0.065 Gm.	1 gr.
50 mg.	0.05 Gm.	3/4 to 4/5 gr.
40 mg.	0.04 Gm.	3/5 to 16/25 gr.
30 mg.	0.03 Gm.	9/20 to 12/25 gr. or 1/2 gr.
25 mg.	0.025 Gm.	3/8 to 2/5 gr.
20 mg.	0.02 Gm.	3/10 to 8/25 gr. or 1/3 gr.
15 mg.	0.015 Gm.	9/40 to 6/25 gr. or 1/4 gr.
12 mg.	0.012 Gm.	9/50 to 24/125 gr. or 1/5 gr.
10 mg.	0.010 Gm.	3/20 to 4/25 gr. or 1/6 gr.
8 mg.	0.008 Gm.	3/25 to 16/125 gr. or 1/8 gr.
6 mg.	0.006 Gm.	9/100 to 12/125 gr. or 1/10 gr.
5 mg.	0.005 Gm.	3/40 to 2/25 gr. or 1/12 gr.
4 mg.	0.004 Gm.	3/50 to 8/125 gr. or 1/15 to 1/16 gr.
3 mg.	0.003 Gm.	9/200 to 6/125 gr. or 1/20 gr.
2 mg.	0.002 Gm.	3/100 to 4/125 gr. or 1/30 gr.
1.5 mg.	0.0015 Gm.	9/400 to 3/125 gr. or 1/40 gr.
1.2 mg.	0.0012 Gm.	9/500 to 12/625 gr. or 1/50 gr.
1 mg.	0.001 Gm.	3/200 to 2/125 gr. or 1/60, 1/64, or 1/65 gr.

TABLE 6. ADDITIONAL APPROXIMATE METRIC–APOTHECARIES'
WEIGHT EQUIVALENTS (CONTINUED)

Metric		*Apothecaries'
0.8 mg.	0.0008 Gm.	3/250 to 8/625 gr. or 1/80 gr.
0.6 mg.	0.0006 Gm.	9/1000 to 6/625 gr. or 1/100 gr.
0.5 mg.	0.0005 Gm.	1/120, 1/128, or 1/130 gr.
0.4 mg.	0.0004 Gm.	3/500 to 4/625 gr. or 1/150 to 1/160 gr.
0.3 mg.	0.0003 Gm.	9/2000 to 3/625 gr. or 1/200 to 1/210 gr.
0.25 mg.	0.00025 Gm.	3/800 to 1/250 gr.
0.2 mg.	0.0002 Gm.	3/1000 to 2/625 gr. or 1/300 to 1/320 gr.
0.15 mg.	0.00015 Gm.	9/4000 to 3/1250 gr. or 1/400 gr.
0.12 mg.	0.00012 Gm.	9/5000 to 6/3125 gr. or 1/500 gr.
0.1 mg.	0.0001 Gm.	3/2000 to 1/625 gr. or 1/600, 1/640, or 1/650 gr.

*Often when using both 15 and 16 grains = 1 gram to determine these grain
equivalents, the answer is a fraction which is awkward to use. In such instances,
a nearly equal, simplified fraction also has been given.

TABLE 7. EXACT METRIC–APOTHECARIES' EQUIVALENTS

Metric	Apothecaries'
31.1035 Gm.	1 oz.
1. Gm.	15.432 gr.
0.972 Gm.	15 gr.
0.648 Gm.	10 gr.
0.324 Gm.	5 gr.
0.0648 Gm.	1 gr.
1 ml.	16.23 m.

APPENDIX B
ABBREVIATIONS USED IN DRUG ADMINISTRATION

Abbreviation	Meaning	Abbreviation	Meaning
āā	of each	o.h. or q.h.	every hour
a.c.	before meals	o.m. or q. a.m.	every morning
ad.	up to	o.n. or q. p.m.	every night
ad lib.	as desired	O.S.	left eye
aq.	water	os	mouth
aq. dest. or D.W.	distilled water	oz.	ounce
b.i.d.	twice a day	p.c.	after meals
c̄	with	per	by
caps.	capsules	per os or p.o.	by mouth
comp.	compound	pil.	pill
dil.	dilute	p.r.n.	when required
elix.	elixir	q.h.	every hour
ext.	extract	q.2h.	every 2 hours
fld. or fl.	fluid	q.3h.	every 3 hours
Ft.	make	q.4h.	every 4 hours
Gm.	gram	q.i.d.	four times a day
gr.	grain	q.s.	quantity sufficient
gtt.	drop	℞	take
H.	by hypodermic	s̄	without
h. or hr.	hour	s.c.	subcutaneously
h.s.	hour of sleep	Sig. or S.	write on label
I.M.	intramuscularly	sol.	solution
I.V.	intravenously	s.o.s.	once if necessary
M.	mix	sp.	spirits
m.	minim	ss	a half
mixt. or mist.	mixture	stat.	immediately
n., noc. or noct.	night	syr.	syrup
non rep.	not to be repeated	t.i.d.	three times a day
O	pint	tr. or tinct.	tincture
ol.	oil	U.	unit
O.D.	right eye	ung.	ointment
o.d. or q.d.	every day	vin.	wine

APPENDIX C

ARITHMETIC REVIEW

PRETEST IN ARITHMETIC

Which is larger?

1. 1/150 or 1/200?

2. 3/7 or 3/8?

3. 100/1 or 3/2?

4. 0.006 or 0.03?

5. 1:20 or 1:2?

6. 1/10% or 1/5%?

Complete the following.

7. 2/7 + 2/3 =

8. 1/100 + 1/100 =

9. 1-1/2 + 3/4 =

10. 1/2 + 1/3 + 1-1/4 =

11. 1/4% + 1/3% =

12. 0.04 + 0.033 =

13. 1:5 + 4:6 =

14. 1/100 − 1/150 =

15. 4/3 − 7/6 =

16. 1-1/2 − 1-1/3 =

17. 0.66 − 0.06 =

18. 1/1000 x 1 =

19. 0.03 x 2 =

20. 100/1 x 5 =

21. 2/3 x 1/2 =

22. 1-1/2 x 1/3 =

23. 1-1/2 ÷ 1/3 =

24. 300/150 ÷ 2 =

25. 3/4 ÷ 2/3 =

26. 1.5 ÷ 0.1 =

27. 0.5 ÷ 3/4 =

28. $\dfrac{1/3}{1/2} =$

29. $\dfrac{1\text{-}1/2}{2} =$

Change to decimal fractions.

30. 1/10

31. 2%

32. 15/1

33. 2:50

Change to ratios.

34. 1

35. 75%

36. 1/1000

37. 0.5%

38. 0.125%

Change to per cent.

39. 1/300

40. 1/2

41. 1 : 1000

42. 0.75

43. 2-1/2

Solve for x, the unknown value.

44. 400 : 1 = 1000 : x

45. 80 : 16 = 100 : x

46. 15 : 1000 = x : 100

47. $\dfrac{1}{10,000} : \dfrac{1}{8000} = x : 4000$

48. 100 : 1000 = 1/4 : x

Round off to the nearest hundredth.

49. 0.666-2/3

50. 0.3-1/3

COMMON FRACTIONS

A proper fraction is one in which the numerator is less than the denominator, e.g., 1/2, 3/4, 2/3, 5/6, 1/200.

An improper fraction is one in which the numerator is equal to, or greater than, the denominator, e.g., 2/2, 7/5, 300/150.

A mixed number is a whole number plus a fraction, e.g., 1-1/3, 2-1/2, 10-2/3, 25-7/8.

A mixed number can be changed to an improper fraction by multiplying the whole number by the denominator, adding the numerator, and placing the sum over the denominator, e.g., $1\text{-}1/3 = \dfrac{3 \times 1 + 1}{3} = 4/3$.

An improper fraction can be changed to a whole or a mixed number by dividing the numerator by the denominator, e.g., 7/5 = 7 ÷ 5 = 1-2/5.

A whole number has an unexpressed denominator of 1, e.g., 4=4/1, 1=1/1, 1000 = 1000/1.

A complex fraction is one in which the numerator, the denominator, or both, are fractions, e.g., $\dfrac{1\text{-}1/2}{2}, \dfrac{1/1000}{1}, \dfrac{1/3}{1/2}, \dfrac{1}{1/100}$.

To simplify a complex fraction divide the numerator by the denominator after reducing either or both, as needed, to a simpler fraction, e.g.,

$$\frac{1\text{-}1/2}{2} = \frac{3/2}{2} = \quad 3/2 \div 2/1 = 3/2 \text{ x } 1/2 = 3/4.$$

To add common fractions change fractions to equivalent fractions with the least common denominator, add the numerators, and write this sum over the common denominator. A least common denominator is the smallest number into which all denominators can be divided evenly.

Adding proper fractions:
  $1/300 + 1/150 + 1/10 = 1/300 + 2/300 + 30/300 = 33/300$

Adding improper fractions:
  $1/1 + 4/3 + 9/7 = 21/21 + 28/21 + 27/21 = 76/21$

Adding mixed numbers:
  $1\text{-}1/3 + 2\text{-}1/2 = 4/3 + 5/2 = 8/6 + 15/6 = 23/6$

Adding whole numbers and fractions:
  $2 + 1/2 = 2/1 + 1/2 = 4/2 + 1/2 = 5/2 = 2\text{-}1/2$

To subtract common fractions again reduce to equivalent fractions with the least common denominator, subtract the numerator with the minus sign from the other numerator and place the remainder over the common denominator.

Subtracting proper fractions:
  $1/150 - 1/300 = 2/300 - 1/300 = 1/300$

Subtracting improper fractions:
  $3/2 - 5/4 = 6/4 - 5/4 = 1/4$

Subtracting mixed numbers:
  $1\text{-}1/3 - 1\text{-}1/4 = 4/3 - 5/4 = 16/12 - 15/12 = 1/12$ or

$$4\text{-}3/4 - 2\text{-}1/2 = 4\text{-}3/4 = \begin{array}{r} 4\text{-}3/4 \\ -2\text{-}2/4 \\ \hline 2\text{-}1/4 \end{array} \quad \text{or}$$
$$\phantom{4\text{-}3/4 - 2\text{-}1/2 =} \begin{array}{r} -2\text{-}1/2 \end{array}$$

$$4\text{-}1/2 - 2\text{-}3/4 = \begin{array}{r} 4\text{-}1/2 \\ -2\text{-}3/4 \end{array} = \begin{array}{r} 4\text{-}2/4 \\ -2\text{-}3/4 \end{array} = \begin{array}{r} 3\text{-}6/4 \\ -2\text{-}3/4 \\ \hline 1\text{-}3/4 \end{array}$$

Subtracting whole numbers and fractions:
$$5 - 2\text{-}1/2 = 5/1 - 5/2 = 10/2 - 5/2 = 5/2 = 2\text{-}1/2 \quad \text{or}$$

$$\begin{array}{r} 5 - 2\text{-}1/2 = 5 \\ - \ 2\text{-}1/2 \\ \hline \end{array} = \begin{array}{r} 4\text{-}2/2 \\ - \ 2\text{-}1/2 \\ \hline 2\text{-}1/2 \end{array}$$

To multiply common fractions multiply the numerators together and the denominators together then reduce the resulting fraction to its lowest terms.

Multiplying proper fractions:
$$2/3 \times 3/4 = 6/12 = 1/2 \quad \text{or} \quad 1/1000 \times 1/2 = 1/2000$$

Multiplying improper fractions:
$$2/1 \times 3/2 = 6/2 = 3 \quad \text{or} \quad 300/150 \times 1/1 = 300/150 = 2$$

Multiplying mixed numbers:
$$1\text{-}1/3 \times 2\text{-}1/2 = 4/3 \times 5/2 = 20/6 = 3\text{-}2/6 = 3\text{-}1/3$$

Multiplying whole numbers by fractions:
$$2 \times 1/100 = 2/1 \times 1/1000 = 2/1000 = 1/500 \quad \text{or}$$
$$1 \times 1/2 = 1/1 \times 1/2 \quad \text{or} \quad 1/200 \times 2 = 1/200 \times 2/1 = 2/200 = 1/100$$

To divide common fractions invert the divisor and multiply.

Dividing proper fractions:
$$2/3 \div 3/4 = 2/3 \times 4/3 = 8/9 \quad \text{or} \quad 1/2 \div 1/2 = 1/2 \times 2/1 = 2/2 = 1$$

Dividing improper fractions:
$$3/2 \div 2/1 = 3/2 \times 1/2 = 3/4 \quad \text{or}$$
$$300/150 \div 2/1 = 300/150 \times 1/2 = 300/300 = 1$$

Dividing mixed numbers:
$$1\text{-}1/2 \div 2\text{-}1/3 = 3/2 \div 7/3 = 3/2 \times 3/7 = 9/14$$

Dividing whole numbers and fractions:
$$100 \div 1/2 = 100/1 \div 1/2 = 100/1 \times 2/1 = 200 \quad \text{or}$$
$$1/2 \div 100 = 1/2 \div 100/1 = 1/2 \times 1/100 = 1/200$$

To compare sizes of fractions is often very important for nurses.

If numerators are the same the fraction with the smaller denominator represents the larger value, e.g., 1/2 is larger than 1/4 and 1/150 is larger than 1/300. Fractions with different denominators can be compared by changing to the same denominator, e.g., 1/150 and 1/300 to 2/300 and 1/300 or 1/2 and 1/4 to 2/4 and 1/4.

If denominators are the same the fraction with the larger numerator represents the larger value, e.g., 2/300 is larger than 1/300.

DECIMAL FRACTIONS

A decimal fraction is one or more of the ten parts of the units of tenths.

Changing common fractions to decimal fractions is done by dividing the numerator by the denominator, e.g.,

$$1/2 = 2 \overline{)1.0}^{\,.5} \qquad \underline{or} \qquad 1/200 = 200 \overline{)1.000}^{\,.005}$$

Changing decimal fractions to common fractions is done more easily but great caution should be taken in determining the correct denominator, as shown below.

.1	= 1/10	or one-tenth
.01	= 1/100	or one-hundredth
.001	= 1/1000	or one-thousandth
.0001	= 1/10,000	or one ten-thousandth
.741	= 741/1000	
.3	= 3/10	
.4276	= 4276/10,000	
.005	= 5/1000	

To add and subtract decimals place the decimal points in vertical alignment.

Adding decimals:

$$.0004 + .006 = \begin{array}{r} .0004 \\ .006 \\ \hline .0064 \end{array}$$

Subtracting decimals:

$$.06 - .004 = \begin{array}{r} .060 \\ .004 \\ \hline .056 \end{array}$$

To multiply decimals first multiply as with whole numbers; then, point off from the right in the product as many decimal places as there are in both the multiplier and the multiplicand.

Multiplying decimals:

$$1.25 \times .75 = \begin{array}{r} 1.25 \\ \underline{.75} \\ 625 \\ \underline{875} \\ .9375 \end{array}$$

To divide decimals divide as with whole numbers after converting the divisor to a whole number by moving the decimal point to the far right and after moving the decimal point in the dividend the same number of places to the right, adding zeros as necessary.

Dividing decimals:

$$1.125 \div .75 = .75 \overline{)1.125} = 75 \overline{)112.5} \begin{array}{r} 1.5 \\ \underline{75} \\ 375 \\ \underline{375} \end{array}$$

or

$$.6 \div .03 = .03 \overline{).6} = 3 \overline{)60.} \begin{array}{r} 20. \\ \underline{60} \end{array}$$

PERCENTAGE

A per cent is a part of 100 equal parts. It is a fraction with a denominator of 100.

To change per cent to a common fraction write the per cent as the numerator and replace the % symbol with 100 as the denominator of the fraction, as shown below.

$$5\% = 5/100 = 1/20$$
$$1/10\% = \frac{1/10}{100} = 1/10 \div 100/1 = 1/10 \times 1/100 = 1/1000$$
$$.2\% = \frac{2/10}{100} = 2/10 \div 100/1 = 2/10 \times 1/100 = 2/1000 = 1/500$$

To change common fractions to per cent divide the numerator by the denominator and multiply the quotient by 100 (move decimal point 2 places to the right), as shown below.

$$1/8 = 8 \overline{)1.000} \begin{array}{c} .125 \end{array} = .125 \times 100 = 12.5\%$$

$$3/5 \quad = 5\overline{)3.0}^{.6} = .6 \times 100 = 60\%$$

$$1/1000 \quad = 1000\overline{)1.000}^{.001} = .001 \times 100 = .1\%$$

To change per cent to decimal fractions drop the per cent sign and divide by 100 (move decimal point 2 places to the left), as shown below.

$$12.5\% \quad = .125$$
$$60\% \quad = .6$$
$$.1\% \quad = .001$$

RATIO AND PROPORTION

A ratio is the same as a fraction. A proportion consists of two ratios or fractions which are equal in value. The ratio 1 : 20 means that in every 20 parts of a substance (solvent, e.g.) there is one equal part of another substance (solute, e.g.). The ratio 1 : 20 equals the ratio 5 : 100 and these two ratios have the same relative values or are in proportion, e.g., 1 : 20 = 5 : 100.

The first and last terms of a proportion are called the extremes; the second and third terms, the means. The product of the means equals the product of the extremes. When any three of the four terms are known, one can determine the fourth term.

An unknown mean is found by dividing the product of the extremes by the known mean, as shown below.

$$
\begin{array}{llll}
4 : 20 & = x : 25 & \text{or} & 4 : x = 5 : 25 \\
20x & = 100 & & 5x = 100 \\
\dfrac{20x}{20} & = \dfrac{100}{20} & & x = 20 \\
x & = 5 & &
\end{array}
$$

An unknown extreme is found by dividing the product of the means by the known extreme, as follows.

$$
\begin{array}{llll}
x : 20 & = 5 : 25 & \text{or} & 4 : 20 = 5 : x \\
25x & = 100 & & 4x = 100 \\
\dfrac{25x}{25} & = \dfrac{100}{25} & & x = 25 \\
x & = 4 & &
\end{array}
$$

96

Actually this is the same as saying that after multiplying the means and extremes, one divides both sides of the resulting equation by the number which precedes the x, the unknown value.

A more detailed explanation of the use of ratio and proportion is given in the text of this workbook.

ANSWERS

The answers are provided for use by students and instructors. Sometimes more than one correct answer is given here. Depending upon the equivalents or methods of calculation used, additional correct answers, which are not shown here, may result.

CHAPTER II
PRACTICE PROBLEMS:

p. 13.

1. 1/2 tablet per os 4 times a day
2. 2 capsules by mouth every 6 hrs.
3. 4 tablets orally every 4 hrs.
4. 1/2 of 25-mg. tablet (in order to give least number of tablets possible) by mouth 4 times a day

p. 14.

5. 2 of 10-mg. and 1 of 5-mg. tablets orally 4 times a day
6. 2 of 50-mg. capsules by mouth at hour of sleep as needed and may repeat 1 time
7. 1/2 tablet orally 4 times a day
8. 3 tablets orally 4 times a day

p. 15.

9. 2 tablets by mouth every 4 hrs. for 72 hrs. prior to surgery
10. 1 of 64-mg. and 1 of 32-mg. tablets by mouth 4 times a day
11. 1 of 1/120-gr. tablet by mouth 4 times a day
12. 1 of 100-mg. tablet orally 3 times a day

p. 21.

1. 5 ml. immediately by mouth
2. 0.5 cc. or 8 m. orally 4 times a day
3. 30 cc. orally 4 times a day
4. 5 ml. orally 3 times a day

p. 22.

5. 20 ml. by mouth immediately
6. 2 drams or 8 ml. of the mixture (1 dram of each drug) orally 3 times a day
7. 2 cc. by mouth every 4 hrs. as needed
8. 3.2 m. (0.1 mg. : 16 m. = 0.02 mg. : x m.) or 0.2 ml. orally every day

p. 23.

9. 4 ml. orally every 4 hrs.
10. 4 ml. by mouth every 4 hrs. as needed
11. 10 ml. orally every 6 hrs.
12. 15 ml. by mouth 3 times a day

CHAPTER III
PRACTICE PROBELMS

p. 27.

1. 0.5 ml. of 80 units per ml. intramuscularly every 12 hrs.
2. 3 ml. from 4-ml. (0.8 mg.) ampule (would be less expensive than 3 ml. from 2 of the 2-ml. [0.4 mg.] ampules) intramuscularly every day
3. 2 m. (1/8 ml.) from 2-ml. (0.4 mg.) ampule intramuscularly every day
4. 2 cc. intramuscularly every day

p. 28.

5. 1.5 cc. hypodermically every 4 hrs. as needed for pain
6. 0.1 ml. intradermally at 9 a.m. tomorrow
7. 2 ml. intramuscularly immediately
8. 1.67 (1-2/3) cc. intramuscularly twice a day

p. 29.

9. 1 ml. hypodermically every 3 hrs. as needed for asthma
10. 2 ml. intramuscularly now; then 1 ml. every 6 hrs. as needed for nausea
11. 2 cc. intramuscularly 4 times a day as needed for asthma
12. 2 m. hypodermically at 10 a.m. before surgery

p. 35.

1. Dissolve 1 of the 20-mg. tablets in 20 m. diluent and give 15 m. (or dissolve in 16 m. and give 12 m.) subcutaneously every 3 hrs. as needed for pain.

2. Dissolve 1 of the 3-mg. tablets in 18 m. diluent and give 15 m. (or dissolve in 12 m. and give 10 m.) hypodermically every 3 hrs. as needed for pain.

3. Dissolve 1 of the 1-gr. tablets in 24 m. diluent and give 16 m. (or dissolve in 21 m. and give 14 m., in 18 m. and give 12 m., or in 15 m. and give 10 m.) hypodermically every 3 hrs. as needed for pain.

4. Dissolve 1 of the 1/4-gr. tablets in 32 m. diluent (if 2.5 ml. syringe) and give 8 m. (or dissolve in 24 m., expel all but 6 m. and add 4 m. diluent) hypodermically every 4 hrs. as needed for pain.

p. 36.

5. Dissolve 1 of the 1/4-gr. tablets in as much as 16 m. diluent and give 16 m. (or dissolve in as little as 10 m. and give 10 m.) hypodermically every 4 hrs. as needed for pain.

6. Dissolve 1 of the 1/150-gr. tablets of atropine in 2 ml. Demerol and give hypodermically at 10 a.m. before surgery.

7. Dissolve 1 of the 1/200-gr. scopolamine tablets in 1.5 ml. Demerol and give hypodermically at once or dissolve 1 of the 1/150-gr. scopolamine tablets in the 2 ml. of Demerol and give 1.5 ml. of the solution.

8. Dissolve 1 of the 1/150-gr. scopolamine tablets in 2 ml. Demerol and give 1.5 ml. of this solution hypodermically at once.

p. 37.

9. Dissolve 1 of the 0.0003-Gm. tablets in 30 m. diluent and administer 10 m. immediately by hypodermic injection.

10. Dissolve 1 of the 0.0004-Gm. scopolamine tablets in 2 ml. Demerol and administer 0.6 ml. of this solution hypodermically upon call from operating room. In this problem one wants to give 0.6 ml. of the 2 ml. of Demerol in the ampule and by dissolving the tablet in the 2 ml. of Demerol one can give the correct dosage of scopolamine (0.12 mg. ordered: 0.4 mg. available = x ml. to be given: 2 ml. total diluent, or x = 0.6 ml.). If a problem such as this does not work out as conveniently as this one does, one can dissolve the scopolamine tablet in a sterile diluent, expel the portion not needed, then add the 0.6 ml. of Demerol. Of course, separate injections may be given but this causes unnecessary trauma and discomfort to the patient whenever the drugs are compatible and the amount is reasonable for a single injection.

11. Using a 2.5-ml. syringe dissolve 1 of the 8-mg. tablets in 36 m. diluent, expel all but 9 m. and give this amount hypodermically every 4 hrs. as needed. Using a 2-ml. syringe one could dissolve 1 of the 8-mg. tablets in 24 m., expel all but 6 m., then add 4 m. diluent in order to get the

desired 10 m. minimum amount for administration. Unless very skilled, the chances of making an error may be increased, rather than decreased, by the addition of pure diluent to the prepared medication.

12. Dissolve 2 of the 1/8-gr. tablets in from 16 m. to 20 m. of diluent and give the entire amount. One will need more diluent to dissolve 2 tablets than to dissolve 1 tablet.

p. 44.

1. Add 9.6 ml. sterile diluent to vial, dissolve drug, label "300,000 U./ml." and give 1 ml. intramuscularly every 4 hrs.

2. Add 13.6 ml. diluent, label "200,000 U./ml." and give 1 ml. I.M. every 3 hrs. (Dividing the 3,000,000 U. in the vial by 250,000 U. [per 1 ml.] gives a total volume of 12 ml. Therefore, adding 10.6 ml. solvent yields 12 ml. reconstituted solution so the displacement by the drug is 12 ml. minus 10.6 ml. or 1.4 ml. To prepare a solution containing the ordered dosage of 200,000 U. in 1 ml. one would need to prepare 15 ml. of reconstituted solution, or, 3,000,000 U. ÷ 200,000 U. = 15, or, 200,000 U. : 1 ml. = 3,000,000 U. : x ml., with x = 15 ml. The 15 ml. desired minus the 1.4 ml. displacement leaves 13.6 ml. diluent needed.)

3. There is no information about displacement but it probably will be less than 1 ml. This drug will not dissolve in small amounts of diluent. Therefore, add about 4 ml. diluent, dissolve the drug, withdraw the entire amount of dissolved drug into the 5- or 10-ml. syringe used to introduce the diluent, measure the total amount of reconstituted solution and calculate the U. per ml. by dividing the 40 U. by the ml. measured; label the bottle or vial accordingly. Next, calculate the dosage to be given, e.g., 9 U. calculated : 1 ml. = 4 U. : x ml. or 40 U.: 4.5 ml. measured = 4 U. : x ml. (Each dosage of 4 U. will be 1/10 of the entire amount of reconstituted solution which contains 40 U. of drug. One will be giving approximately 0.5 ml. per dose. Use this as a guide to checking the accuracy of your calculations; it is not accurate enough for use in administration!)

4. If one adds 5.2 cc. diluent there will be more than 5.2 cc. of reconstituted solution. The directions say that adding 5.2 cc. yields a solution containing 50 mg./cc. Therefore, this vial contains more than 250 mg. of drug (50 mg. : 1 ml. = 250 mg. : x ml., with x = 5 ml. which is less than the 5.2 ml. to be added). Since neither the amount of drug displacement nor the amount of extra drug is known, one can only add 5.2 cc. of the accompanying solvent and administer 4 cc. of the reconstituted solution intramuscularly immediately. Even though the amount is large it may safely be given as a single injection.

p. 45.

5. Add 1.2 ml. diluent to a 500-mg. vial, measure the total amount and administer 4/5 the total amount intramuscularly. Discard remaining solution and repeat above procedure every 6 hrs.

6. Adding 5.7 ml. will yield 8 ml. (500 mg. : 1 ml. = 4000 mg. : x ml.). The displacement is 2.3 ml. If one wants to reconstitute 4 ml. (1 Gm./ml.), add 1.7 ml. diluent, label the vial "1 Gm./ml." and give 1 ml. intramuscularly every 4 hrs. If this drug does not dissolve in 1.7 ml., add 4 ml. more of diluent (a total of 5.7 ml.), label "500 mg./ml." and administer 2 ml. each time.

7. Adding 5.7 ml. will yield 6 ml. (1.5 ml. : 250 mg. = x ml. : 1000 mg.). The displacement is 0.3 ml. Add 1.7 ml. to get 2 ml. reconstituted solution, label "500 mg./ml." and give 1 ml. intramuscularly every 6 hrs. If the drug will not dissolve in 1.7 ml., add 2 ml. more of diluent, label "250 mg./ml." and give 2 ml. each time. Either way there are two doses in each vial.

8. Adding 4 ml. yields 4.4 ml. (two 0.5 Gm. doses of 2.2 ml. each). To have 100 mg. in 1 ml., one needs 10 ml. so add 9.6 ml. diluent, label "100 mg./ml." and give 1 ml. intramuscularly every 6 hrs.

p. 46.

9. To give the ordered dosage in 1 ml. one should add 2.9 ml. diluent but the drug will not go into solution if less than 4 ml. is used. Therefore, use 4.6 ml. diluent, label "200 mg./ml." and administer 1.5 ml. intramuscularly every 6 hrs., or add 4 ml. diluent, label "227 mg./ml." or "0.5 Gm. in 2.2 ml." and administer 1.32 ml. each time.

10. Add 2 ml. diluent, measure total amount, give 1/2 total amount intramuscularly now and label remainder properly for administration in 12 hrs.

11. The amount of displacement by this drug is very little but to ensure accuracy add 1 to 1.5 ml., measure total amount, give 3/5 of total amount intramuscularly every night at bedtime.

12. Use 2.1 ml. diluent, label "400,000 U./ml." and give 1 ml. intramuscularly every 3 hrs. If the drug will not dissolve use 4.6 ml. diluent, label "200,000 U./ml." and administer 2 ml. each time.

p. 51.

1. Give 0.1 ml. U.40 regular insulin subcutaneously 20 min. before meals 3 times a day, preferably with a tuberculin syringe.

2. Give 7.2 m. U.40 P.Z.I. insulin subcutaneously at 4 p.m. every day with a tuberculin or hypodermic syringe or fill an insulin syringe to the 36-U. mark on the U.80 scale.

3. Give 2 m. of U.40 regular insulin, preferably with tuberculin rather than hypodermic syringe because of the small amount.

4. Using U.40 zinc insulin, fill insulin syringe to the 24-U. mark on the U.40 scale and give subcutaneously 1 hr. before breakfast each day.

p. 52.

5. Using U. 80 N.P.H. insulin fill insulin syringe to 45-U. mark on the U.80 scale; then, using U.80 regular insulin, continue to fill syringe to the 69-U. mark on the U.80 scale and administer subcutaneously 1 hr. before breakfast tomorrow.

6. The 1-ml. insulin syringe will not hold the ordered amount. Therefore, give 18.4 m. of lente insulin, with a hypodermic syringe, 1 hr. before breakfast every day.

7. Using the U.80 Ultra-lente insulin fill the syringe to the U.65 mark of the U.80 scale and give 1 hr. before breakfast tomorrow.

8. Give 7.2 m. of U.40 Semi-lente insulin subcutaneously 1/2 hr. before breakfast q.d., preferably with a tuberculin syringe.

p. 53.

9. Use U.80 Ultra-lente insulin and fill the syringe to the U.46 mark on the U.80 scale and give subcutaneously 1 hr. before breakfast every day.

10. Give 6 m. regular insulin plus 12 m. N.P.H. insulin (total of 18 m.) subcutaneously with hypodermic syringe 1/2 hr. before breakfast each morning. If one has a 3-ml. insulin syringe, use U.40 regular insulin to the 15-U. mark and add U.40 N.P.H. insulin to the 45-U. mark, both on the U.40 scale on the syringe.

11. Give 0.9 ml. of U.40 regular insulin subcutaneously 15 min. before meals 3 times a day.

12. Use U.80 lente insulin to the 35-U. mark on the U.80 scale and add U.80 regular insulin to the 45-U. mark on the U.80 scale and administer subcutaneously 20 min. before breakfast daily.

p. 58.

1. 62.5 or 62 or 63 drops per minute
2. 166-2/3 or 167 drops per minute
3. 41-2/3 or 42 drops per minute
4. 31-1/4 or 31 drops per minute

p. 59.

5. 29-1/6 or 29 drops per minute
6. 16-2/3 or 17 drops per minute

7. 27-7/9 or 28 drops per minute
8. 26-2/3 or 27 drops per minute

p. 60.

9. 33-1/3 or 33 drops per minute
10. 33-1/3 or 33 drops per minute. It is right on schedule.
11. 10 drops per minute
12. 20-5/6 or 21 drops per minute

CHAPTER IV
PRACTICE PROBLEMS:

p. 67.

1. Dissolve 9 ml. or 2 tsp. (9 Gm.)|sodium chloride in 1 qt. of tap water at correct temperature.
2. Dissolve 60 ml. or 2 oz. (60 Gm.) sodium bicarbonate in 2 qts. of sterile water (if available) at correct temperature.
3. Dissolve 2 of the 0.5-Gm. mercury bichloride tablets in 1000 ml. sterile distilled water.
4. Dissolve 10 of the 30-mg. gentian violet tablets in 1 oz. of water, preferably sterile.

p. 68.

5. Dissolve 1 of 5-gr. and 1 of 1-gr. $KMNO_4$ tablets in 1 gal. or 4000 ml. of water.
6. Dissolve 2 of the 1-gr. $KMNO_4$ tablets in 1 qt. of sterile water.
7. Dissolve 1 of the 5-gr. $KMNO_4$ tablets in 5000 ml. sterile water or make 1000 ml. stronger stock solution and dilute this for each treatment.
8. Dissolve 12.5 ml. (12.5 Gm.) of dextrose powder in 250 ml. water.

p. 72.

1. Use 100 ml. of the 1:1000 Zephiran Cl and 400 ml. of water.
2. Use 30 ml. of the 10% dextrose and 90 ml. of water.
3. Use 833-1/3 ml. of the 1:10,000 $KMNO_4$ and 166-2/3 ml. of sterile water.
4. Use 2947-7/19 ml. of 95% alcohol and 1052-12/19 ml. of water.

p. 73.

5. Use 1 part 1:100 Adrenalin and 9 parts water.
6. Use 10 ml. hydrogen peroxide (3%) and 20 ml. of water.

7. Use 200 ml. of 5% Dakin's solution and 1800 ml. of water.
8. Use 200 ml. of 5% boric acid solution and 300 ml. sterile water.

CHAPTER V
REVIEW PROBLEMS:

p. 74.

1. Administer 2.25 ml. (if using 1 gr. = 60 mg.) intramuscularly immediately or 2.4375 ml. (if using 1 gr. = 65 mg.).
2. 20-5/6 or 21 drops per minute
3. Give 1.25 ml. of the U.40 lente insulin subcutaneously 1 hr. before breakfast tomorrow using a hypodermic syringe.
4. Administer 2 of the 5-gr. ASA tablets orally every 3 to 4 hrs. as needed.

p. 75.

5. Dissolve the Bejectal as directed and administer 1 ml. intramuscularly 2 times a week. There is only one type, size, or strength of Bejectal available if it is mixed as directed.
6. Use 2666-2/3 ml. of the 1:8000 $KMNO_4$ and 1333-1/3 ml. of water.
7. Administer 2 ml. Nembutal, 1.5 ml. Demerol, and 1 of the 1/150-gr. atropine tablets hypodermically on call.
8. Administer 0.6 ml. Kantrex intramuscularly every 12 hrs.

p. 76.

9. Give 12 ml. (if using 32 ml. per oz.) Kaon 3 times a day.
10. Add 18 Gm. (1 tbsp. or 4 tsp.) of salt to 2 qts. of tap water at the proper temperature and administer.
11. Add 2.1 ml. sterile diluent to vial, dissolve drug, label vial "400,000 U./ml." and give 1 ml. intramuscularly every 4 hrs.
12. Administer 1 of the 30-mg. phenobarbital sodium tablets orally 4 times a day.

CHAPTER VI
PRACTICE PROBLEMS:

p. 81.

1. The 50 mg. per day ordered exceeds maximum of 20.45 mg. calculated. This may be an initial rather than a sustaining dose.
2. The 3-mg. dose ordered is a little less than the 3.3 mg. calculated.

3. The 0.02 ordered is exactly the same as the 0.02 calculated.
4. The 0.025 mg. ordered is less than the 0.167 mg. calculated. See Problem 5.

p. 82.

5. The 0.025 mg. ordered is less than the 0.08 mg. calculated.
6. The 100 mg. ordered is 2 to 4 times the calculated amounts of 25 mg. and 50 mg.
7. The 30 mg. ordered is within the range of 20 mg. to 40 mg. calculated.
8. The 0.1 mg. ordered is more than the 0.067 mg. calculated.

APPENDIX C

PRETEST IN ARITHMETIC

p. 90.

1.	1/150	26.	15
2.	3/7	27.	2/3 or 0.67
3.	100/1	28.	2/3
4.	0.03	29.	3/4
5.	1 : 2	30.	0.1
6.	1/5%	31.	0.02
7.	20/21	32.	15.0
8.	1/50	33.	.04
9.	2-1/4	34.	1 : 1
10.	2-1/12	35.	75 : 100 or 3 : 4
11.	7/12%	36.	1 : 1000
12.	0.073	37.	5 : 1000 or 1 : 200
13.	13/15	38.	1 : 800
14.	1/300	39.	1/3%
15.	1/6	40.	50%
16.	1/6	41.	1/10%
17.	0.60	42.	75%
18.	1/1000	43.	250%
19.	0.06	44.	2-1/2
20.	500	45.	20
21.	1/3	46.	1-1/2
22.	1/2	47.	3200
23.	4-1/2	48.	2-1/2
24.	1	49.	0.67
25.	1-1/8	50.	0.33

106